D0685909

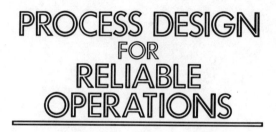

PROCESS DESIGN
FOR
RELIABLE
OPERATIONS

Gulf Publishing Company
Book Division
Houston, London, Paris, Tokyo

PROCESS DESIGN
FOR
RELIABLE
OPERATIONS

Norman P. Lieberman

PROCESS DESIGN FOR RELIABLE OPERATIONS

Copyright © 1983 by Gulf Publishing Company, Houston, Texas. All rights reserved. Printed in the United States of America. This book, or parts thereof, may not be reproduced in any form without permission of the publisher.

Second Printing, May 1984

Library of Congress Cataloging in Publication Data
Lieberman, Norman P.
  Process design for reliable operations.
  Includes bibliographical references and index.
  1. Chemical plants—Equipment and supplies—Design and con-
    struction. I. Title.
TP155.5.L54 1983   660.2'81   83-1630
ISBN 0-87201-747-8

Dedication

To Lisa, Joe and little Irene, my children,
To Janet and Mary Ann, my friends,
To Mary and Lou, my parents.

Acknowledgments

To my wonderful, incomparable secretary, Carol Sutton, I give my sincere thanks for helping to assemble this book. To my colleagues at the Good Hope Refinery, I acknowledge their many ideas, which I have freely drawn upon in my writings.

Contents

Preface

Several years ago I noticed that most professional process design engineers had little industrial plant operating experience. Also, field engineers, who must occasionally design process equipment, were not cognizant of practical process design methods.

As computer design technology advances, the fundamental practical aspects of plant process design are becoming a lost art. The primary purpose of this book is to describe how process equipment should be designed so that it will function in an operating plant.

A second purpose is to instill just a trace of doubt in the reader's mind.

It may be possible—and it has certainly been tried—to incorporate the whole of process plant design theory in a single text. However, the practical aspects of process design are so complex and numerous that they are beyond possible total documentation.

The unique approach used in this book will awaken the novice designer to the concept that detailed chemical engineering calculations are only a fraction of his responsibilities. The years of field experience available from operating personnel are the foundation upon which successful plant designs must rest. The designer who absorbs this knowledge will have a practical basis from which he can implement innovative process improvements.

If you have chosen a career as a process plant designer, then you have selected a difficult road. A bewildering, convoluted, yet strangely rewarding journey lies ahead. Perhaps this book may smooth your way.

Norman P. Lieberman

1

What Is a Process Design?

It was Pat's last day at work.

"Coal oil is produced at 350°F, steamboat oil at 550°F, and Foote's oil at 650°F." Chief Process Design Engineer Pat McNamara leaned back in his chair, brushed the sparce gray hair away from his wrinkled forehead, and prepared himself for a lengthy soliloquy.

Pat McNamara was, I imagine, the last process engineer to use the archaic terms of "coal oil" and "steamboat oil" for petroleum distillates. Pat is dead now, but his words and wisdom, honed to a fine sharpness by 40 years of practical process experience, still linger in my mind.

"A process design is more than just a summation of heat and material balance calculations. Because a process plant is more like a living organism than a machine, the process designer plays the part of creator, not just engineer."

Pat lit a large cigar, enveloped us all in a cloud of white smoke, and continued.

"A structure will either stand or fail, and is judged accordingly, but a process plant, like a man, is a collection of compromises, and hence can only approach perfection. The essence of a process design is its control strategy. It serves the same function in an operating plant that our central nervous system does in our bodies. Process plants each have a unique character which reflects the knowledge and experience of the man who designed their controls.

"Next to the control scheme, specification of the physical size of equipment is the most vital part of the process design. Typically, the inexperienced designer will oversize every part of the plant and then undersize an essential flash drum or pump, which then bottlenecks the entire operation.

"The process design specifies the size of such equipment as:

▶ Fractionator towers
▶ Flash drums
▶ Pumps
▶ Compressors
▶ Heat exchangers
▶ Vapor liquid separators
▶ Reactors
▶ Furnaces

"The relative arrangement of the equipment for maximum energy efficiency and capacity is another major function of a process design. Shall a particular pump be located upstream or downstream of a heat exchanger? Is it best to preflash crude prior to product fractionation? These are decisions for the process engineer to make.

"So you can see," Pat concluded, "a process design is really a plan of action, a blueprint, for the other engineering disciplines to follow."

"Then what," I asked, "are the major parts of the plant design which are not the responsibility of the process engineer?"

"Well," Pat answered, "the plot plan, or physical location of pumps, exchangers, towers, etc., is defined by the project engineer. Typically, he is a man with a civil or mechanical engineering degree; process designers almost always are chemical engineers. The project engineer will also size the diameter of the piping and determine the thickness of the vessel walls.

"The instrument engineer will have an electrical engineering background. He will make such important decisions as whether pneumatic (air) or electronic instrumentation will be used. Is it best to control a particular variable with closed-loop computer control, or have a man turning a gate valve in the field? This question is for the instrument engineer to decide.

"Working together, the process, project, and instrument engineers form the project team. This group eventually issues the plant's process & instrumentation diagram (P & ID).

"The P & ID is the fundamental document for building a process unit. Twenty years after a plant has been commissioned, the operators will still be consulting the original P & ID to solve operating problems. But the P & ID is based on the process flowsheet and that brings us back to the process engineer's job.

"Always remember that fallible humans operate a process plant, and the process flowsheet must reflect this weakness. The knowledge to compensate in the process design for human error comes only from years of field experience."

Pat McNamara swiveled 90° to face his beloved chalkboard, which was covered with the powdery remnants of some recent and perhaps final heat balance calculation.

At turns he would write a key word or phrase on the board, then expound on the point, and write something else. It went on that way for an hour.

It may have been his professorial manner, or perhaps it was my reflex as a former student, though to this day I still wonder why I began writing it all down so carefully. My notes follow.

The Elements of a Process Design Package

The model for a process design report is the UOP schedule "A" Package. UOP is a large engineering contractor and their schedule "A" Package is the industry standard for the components of a process design. It consists of:

▶ A process description.
▶ An overall unit material balance listing feeds and products.
▶ A process flowsheet showing major control loops.
▶ A listing of the composition (in mole percent) and quantity (in pounds per hour) of the major process streams. This listing is keyed to the process flowsheet.
▶ A line list giving the design viscosity, specific gravity, temperature, pressure, molecular weight and pounds per hour of every process and utility line.
▶ Heat exchanger data sheets.
▶ A listing of pumps giving the volume to be pumped, the vapor pressure of the fluid, and its specific gravity and viscosity.
▶ Fired heater data sheets, including vaporization curves.
▶ Vessel sketches showing all nozzle locations (but not necessarily sizes).
▶ Tray data sheets for fractionation towers.
▶ Compressor data showing suction and discharge conditions.

Process description. A simple written summary of the purpose of the plant and how it works. This part of the process design package should be written only after all the other components are assembled.

Overall material balance. The amount and physical properties of the plant's feed should be listed, along with expected product yields. All relevant properties of the products should be enumerated.

Process flowsheet. The most important document in a process design package—and frequently the only item that many people look at. A little bit of artistic drafting can be an aid to quick comprehension of the process by someone unfamiliar with the plant. Show control loops for clarity.

Composition summary. Provide a list of the mole-percent composition of every process stream. During the course of the process calculations, these data are developed and the process design package is the place to preserve it for future reference.

Line list. The flows in the line list need not coincide with the flows shown on the process flowsheet. The designer should anticipate that during start-up, a particular line may be required to carry twice its normal flow. Or perhaps during an emergency, a portion of the process may be exposed to unusually high viscosities. The line list is the place for the designer to make sure this insight is built into the plant.

Heat exchanger specifications. For each exchanger a standard TEMA heat exchanger data sheet is filled out. TEMA is the manufacturers' association which sets the standards for shell and tube heat exchangers. The heat-transfer inlet and outlet temperatures and viscosities are the main parameters set. Specification of the fouling factor is also an important, but nebulous, factor.

Pump data. Data tabulated will be used to select centrifugal pumps for each service. Using the maximum expected specific gravity, viscosity, and vapor pressure that can be anticipated for all occasions will result in a centrifugal pump being installed that will perform in adversity.

Fired heater data sheets. Since it is certainly the most costly item of equipment to operate in a process plant. The fired heater or furnace must be specified carefully. The designer sets the maximum allowable heat flux (in $Btu/hr/ft^2$), and this number, along with the heat duty (in Btu/hr), determines the size of the furnace. If vaporization will take place in the heater tubes, then a set of curves describing changes in fluid properties of the oil is required.

Vessel sketches. Trayed towers, reactors, and drums should each be defined by a vessel sketch showing the overall dimensions and distances between the centerlines of all nozzles. It is a good idea to note the locations of manways. You may one day have to crawl through a tower you designed. Details of process internals such as liquid distributors, as well as normal operating temperatures and pressures, are shown on the vessel sketch. The amounts and types of catalyst used are detailed on the reactor vessel sketches, as are the number and spacing of trays in fractionation towers.

Tray data sheets. Fractionation trays will be purchased from a vendor who will need to know the volumes and densities of vapor and liquid streams flowing through each tray of the tower. The designer also specifies the spacing between trays, and the type of tray (bubble cap, valve, sieve) to be employed.

Compressor data sheet. The suction pressure and temperature, the discharge pressure, the gas compressibility, and the ratio of specific heats must be detailed on the compressor data sheet. The discharge temperature is a function of the compressor efficiency and will be calculated by the manufacturer.

Pat fell silent. He toyed with his slide rule, yellowed with age, the numbered scales were illegible with wear. He dropped the ancient instrument in the desk drawer and shuffled his papers into an untidy pile. I left him sitting there; it was Pat's last day at work and we never spoke again.

2

Packed Column Pitfalls

The metal rings lay in a disorderly pile across the road from the refinery manager's office. The manager, Mr. Hasselback, stared out of his window at the bent and crushed rings.

"You know," began Mr. Hasselback, "that tower ran fine for 16 years. Day after day we made on-spec gasoline, kerosene, and diesel oil. Then some engineer comes down here from Chicago and tells us that he can expand our crude running capacity by 20%."

Turning away from the depressing mass of twisted metal, Mr. Hasselback continued, "So that nut from Chicago tells us that we have to replace the trays in our crude tower with 3-inch metal rings. We pulled out 32 perfectly good, two-pass valve trays and replaced them with 6 sections of packing consisting of 3-inch perforated metal rings."

Warming to his subject, Mr. Hasselback's face flushed with anger. "We modified our crude tower internals exactly to the specifications of that crazy Yankee. He was right about one thing—we could run a lot more crude through our tower. The only trouble was that it no longer fractionated. We couldn't control our naphtha end point to make reformer feed, our kerosene didn't meet flash specifications, and our diesel oil contained so much gas oil that we couldn't sell it.

"Now packed crude columns may work fine up North," concluded Mr. Hasselback, "but here in Texas we need trayed towers. So you just go back to Chicago and tell the Vice-President to buy us a new set of valve trays for our crude unit."

I knew what had happened. The refinery operators had been careless during the crude unit start-up. They had allowed a pressure surge to develop (probably due to the sudden flashing and expansion of water to steam) and had upset the packed metal rings inside the tower. Trying not to look at the

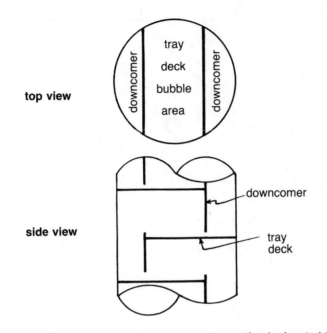

top view

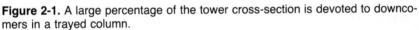

side view

Figure 2-1. A large percentage of the tower cross-section is devoted to downcomers in a trayed column.

dirty mass of ruined metal rings piled across the road, I unfolded my drawings and began to explain the merits of packed versus trayed towers.

"Packing intrinsically has a greater capacity to handle vapor and liquid loads than a trayed tower. In a packed tower, vapor is the continuous phase, whereas in a trayed tower the liquid phase is continuous. To conduct liquid between trays, downcomers are required. As shown in Figure 2-1, typically 30% of the cross-sectional area of a tower is dedicated to downcomer area. For packed towers, the liquid simply trickles down over the packing.

"Without examining all the contradictory claims of manufacturers, but based on my design and operating experience, a properly designed packed tower can have 20-40% more capacity than a trayed tower with an equal number of fractionation stages.

Structured Packing

"Figure 2-2 shows capacity curves for one company's structured packing.[1] This material consists of mats of thin, corrugated, perforated metal sheets layered together in a vertical pattern. Field data obtained on several crude fractionation towers coincide with calculations made with these curves.

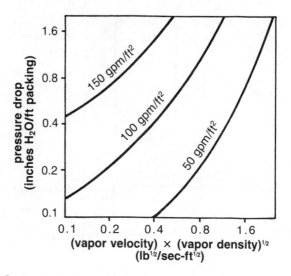

Figure 2-2. Capacity of structured packing with flooding observed at 2½″ H_2O pressure drop.

"This company's structured packing may not be the optimum material available, but it does perform as predicted, both in regard to pressure drop and fractionation. Several other vendors sell competitive packings.

"For the example company's packing, a good rule of thumb for fractionation efficiency is:

► #2 packing provides one equilibrium fractionation stage for each 2½ feet of packing depth.
► #3 packing provides an equilibrium stage for each 3½ feet.
► #4 packing provides an equilibrium stage for each 4½ feet.

Rings Versus Structured Packing

"Structured packing is really the choice material to use in most refinery applications, although Cascade minirings® rings may be more cost effective than structured packing.

"A picture of structured packing is shown in Figure 2-3. The overriding advantage of structured packing is that it comes assembled in large sections (for example, two feet deep, four feet long, and two feet wide). Rings, on the other hand, are several inches in diameter and 1-3 inches high.

"A packed bed of rings is usually supported by a grid of flat iron bars (typically 3 inches high and ⅜ of an inch thick). The bars are set slightly closer together than the size of the rings being supported (see Figure 2-4). The rings are then covered with a chicken wire-type screen to hold them

Figure 2-3. FLEXIPAC® packing. (Courtesy of Koch Engineering Company, Inc. Koch Engineering Company, Inc. manufactures various equipment under the FLEXITRAY®, FLEXIGRID™, and FLEXIPAC® trademarks. FLEXIPAC® elements are manufactured by Koch Engineering Company, Inc. under exclusive license of Sulzer Brothers Ltd., for the U.S.A., Canada, and Mexico.)

down. This arrangement should keep the rings securely in place; however, *in practice* nothing could be further from the truth.

Migrating Rings

"Rings have the obnoxious habit of plugging up pump suctions and getting caught in gate valve seats and control valve inlets. Any one of these problems can shut a plant down. Operating personnel often wonder how the rings find their way from a fractionation tower to remote points in the process piping.

"Rings migrate in two ways. First, rings are easily deformed. During installation, workers assembling the tower internals crush a certain percentage of the rings under their boots. Also, the rings are shipped in burlap bags and are subject to damage. Once partially flattened, the rings slip through the openings in the support grid. They then are washed across a draw-off tray and into a draw-off sump. Once in the draw-off sumps, the rings can migrate to the farthest parts of the plant.

"A more serious form of ring dislocation occurs due to operational upsets. There are several different types of accidents that can upset fractionation tower internals:

▶ A slug of water comes in contact with a pool of hot oil. This incident is commonly encountered on the start-up of low-pressure fractionators.

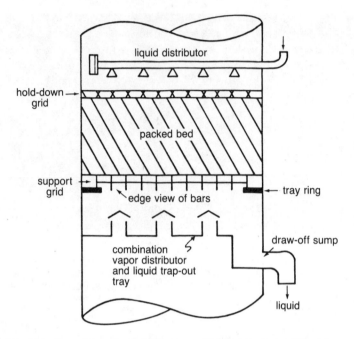

Figure 2-4. Overall arrangement of a packed bed in a fractionation column.

▶ A sudden drop in tower top pressure, such as when a relief valve opens.
▶ The liquid level rises above the reboiler vapor return line and the packed section is bumped by rising gas bubbles, which cause high liquid levels.

Designing Tower Internals

"The proper design of tower internals for a packed column is equal in importance to the selection of the packing itself. These internals consist of a:

▶ Support grid
▶ Hold-down grid
▶ Vapor distributor
▶ Liquid distributor
▶ Liquid trap-out tray

"A typical arrangement of components is shown in Figure 2-4.

Support Grid

"The design of the support grid is a compromise between mechanical integrity and ultimate tower capacity. The capacity of a packed tower is roughly proportional to the open area of the packing.

"For example, a manufacturer lists the open area of 3-inch perforated rings as 75%. (Note that the idea of perforating rings is to increase their open area.) The rings are supported in the tower by a grid consisting of ¼-inch thick bars set on 1¼-inch spacing. This means the open area of the grid is 80%. The open area of the tower at the point that the grid and rings touch is then

$$\text{tower open area} = \text{grid open area} \times \text{ring open area}$$
$$60\% = 80\% \times 75\%$$

"From this calculation, one can see that the designer should minimize the cross-sectional area of the support grid to maximize tower capacity. This is so because the point of contact between the packing and support grid is usually the "pinch" point in the tower. Flooding is initiated above the pinch point in much the same way that a sink "backs-up" due to a partially plugged drain. The capacity of a tower below a pinch point is not affected by flooding above it.

"But, in seeking to minimize the grid cross-sectional area, the mechanical integrity of the grid is reduced."

Mr. Hasselback interrupted my presentation at this point. "You know, you're right. I remember something like that happened to me when I was a young engineer over in Louisiana."

Sensing that I had struck a responsive chord in the refinery manager, I accepted the steaming mug of coffee he poured and settled back to listen to an interesting technical story.

"I've been trying to figure this thing out for 20 years," began Mr. Hasselback, "and while you were talking it suddenly hit me. I was working over in Southern Louisiana as a technical service engineer on a small crude unit. We had a packed section in the tower, a kerosene pumparound, I think. Whenever we raised the kerosene pumparound rate above 12,000 BSD, the packed section would flood."

"How could you tell it was flooding?"

Mr. Hasselback drained his coffee cup and answered, "Well, the tower top temperature would jump up, and the gasoline ASTM end point would also increase. You see, the kerosene would flood up the tower and spill over into the overhead vapor line.

"We learned to tolerate this problem by cutting crude charge, but one problem we could not live with was packing getting caught up in the kerosene pump suction screen. Here, let me draw you a picture of what I mean." As best I can remember it, Mr. Hasselback's sketch is preserved in Figure 2-5.

"We were supporting the packing, 3-inch metal Raschig rings, with a grid made out of bars. Once, when I had a chance to crawl through the tower, I

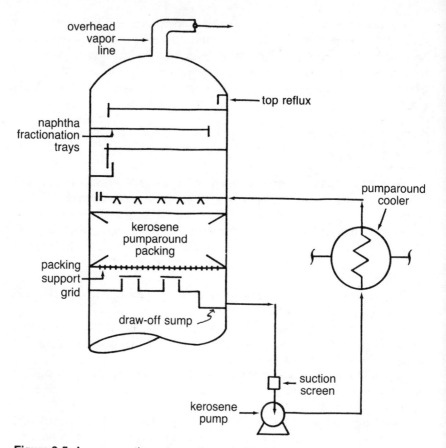

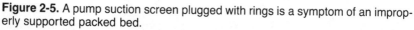

Figure 2-5. A pump suction screen plugged with rings is a symptom of an improperly supported packed bed.

squeezed underneath this support grid and saw how some of the rings could slip through the unevenly spaced bars.

"To correct this problem, I told the Operations Manager, Mr. St. Pierre, that we needed to place a heavy-duty, stainless steel mesh screen over the bars to keep the rings from falling through the support grid."

Mr. Hasselback paused in his story to pour us both another cup of coffee, and then, warmed more by the memories, then by the steaming liquid, he continued. "Well, St. Pierre was a narrow-minded Cajun, and he wasn't interested in my ideas. So I went right over his head to the refinery manager: a good-ole-boy from West Texas. He could see right off how the mesh screen would prevent the rings from falling through the grid.

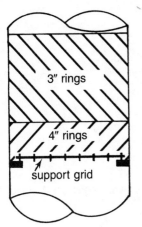

Figure 2-6. A layer of larger rings between the support grid and the main packed bed increases tower capacity.

"So we installed a screen consisting of ⅛-inch wires on a 1-inch × 1-inch square spacing on top of the support grid. A screen with that configuration has about a 75% open area.

"A few days later, my phone rang at 2:00 a.m. I dragged myself out of bed to talk to Mr. St. Pierre. He wanted me to explain why the kerosene pumparound section, which used to flood at 12,000-BSD circulation, was now flooding at 9000 BSD," said Mr. Hasselback.

"You decreased the tower open area by 25%," I interjected, "when you laid the screen over the grid":

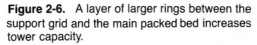

$$\frac{12,000 \text{ BSD} - 9000 \text{ BSD}}{12,000 \text{ BSD}} = 25\%$$

"Yes, I see that now," sighed Mr. Hasselback, "it was a mistake to reduce the percent open area of the tower at the pinch point. That screen induced premature flooding of the kerosene pumparound section. Well, St. Pierre gave me a week to restore the kerosene pumparound to 12,000 BSD, and when I couldn't do it, that Cajun fired me.

"It's a little late to make suggestions," I volunteered, "but the proper way to solve the problem would be to lay a larger-size packing across the grid." I sketched out something equivalent to Figure 2-6.

"In your case, a 12-inch layer of 4-inch metal Raschig rings spread across the support grid would have resulted in a dual benefit: (1) the 4-inch rings would have properly supported the 3-inch rings, but they could not have slipped through the grid; and (2) the 4-inch rings have a larger open area (about 15%) than the 3-inch rings. They would have increased the open area

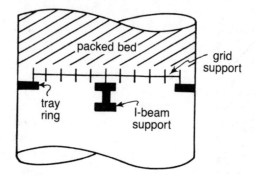

Figure 2-7. I-beams and tray rings can significantly reduce the capacity of a packed column.

of the tower at the grid-rings interface, and hence increased the maximum kerosene pumparound circulation above the 12,000-BSD limit.

"Of course, you would have lost a fraction of a theoretical equilibrium stage (about 7%, assuming a 4-foot high packed section) with the larger rings. That's because the HETP (height of packing equivalent to a theoretical plate) is greater for 4-inch packing relative to 3-inch packing. But that amount of lost contacting efficiency wouldn't be significant in kerosene pumparound service.

Other Ideas to Increase the Capacity of Packed Towers

"One of the big advantages of structured packing is ease of support. The structured packing comes in blocks, typically 24 inches high, 18 inches wide, and 4 feet long. The side pieces are shaped to fit the inside circumference of the tower. A block of this dimension can be supported with a grid construction of support bars spaced one-foot apart. This results in greater ultimate tower capacity.

"One frequent omission made by process designers in sizing packed towers is not allowing for the cross-sectional area of tray rings and beam supports (see Figure 2-7). In small-diameter towers (6-7 feet) the packing support grid rests on a tray ring. Although the tray ring may be only 3 inches wide, this represents 20% of the cross-sectional area of a 5-foot diameter column.

"In larger fractionation towers the packing support grid must be supported by I-beams welded to the sides of the column. The wider the column and the greater the height of packing (and hence its weight), the more numerous and massive these I-beams become. Of course, the cross-sectional area of the beams must also be subtracted from the tower's capacity. The process designer must work closely with the mechanical designer to allow for these restrictions.

Hold-Down Grids

"Most of the hold-down grids that I have seen supplied by vendors for packed towers are wholly inadequate. Some have had the structural strength of chicken wire, others, while strong enough, had bars spaced too wide apart to prevent the upward migration of ring packing.

"Theoretically, there is no reason for the hold-down grid to be very strong. It is not supporting the weight of the packing, as the support grid must. The upward force it must withstand during normal operation is the packed section pressure drop less the weight of the packing itself less the weight of the liquid held up in the packing:

$$F_{HD} = \Delta P_p - W_P - L_h$$

where:
ΔP_p = upward force the vapor exerts on the packed bed.
W_p = weight of the packing.
L_h = weight of liquid held up in the packed bed.
F_{HD} = upward force on hold-down grid.

"During normal operations, the packing's own weight will keep it in place. However, during a unit upset, such as the surge in pressure which accompanies a slug of liquid water entering a hot crude column, ΔP_p can greatly exceed W_p."

I stopped talking. The ensuing silence emphasized my point.

"I guess that's what happened to us," Mr. Hasselback began gloomily, gesturing at the forlorn pile of packing lying across the road. "You know, most of the packing we pulled out of that tower was found on top of the hold-down grid—not underneath the support grid. But in our case, the hold-down grid was strong enough; when we opened the tower, we found the sections of the hold-down grid intact. They had all been clamped to the tray ring and to an I-beam running across the center of the tower. Almost all the little clamps had broken loose, and allowed the packing hold-down grid sections to separate.

"I suppose," he concluded, "we will have to reexamine our operating procedures to prevent pressure surges from upsetting the hold-down grid again. Naturally, a pressure surge will wreck a trayed tower just as easily as a packed tower."

"Let me suggest," I interjected, "that you spot weld the sections of the hold-down grid in place. Also, when you replace the hold-down grid clamps, weld the nuts in place. To really ensure that the hold-down grid stays put, I

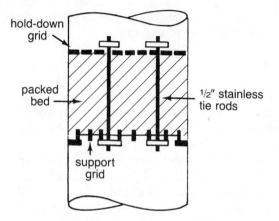

Figure 2-8. Inserting tie rods through a packed bed increases its resistance to damaging pressure surges.

have seen one refiner attach the hold-down grid to the support grid with vertical one-half-inch stainless steel rods. Let me draw you a picture of what I mean" (see Figure 2-8).

Vapor Distributor

"In large-diameter packed towers (more than 4-6 feet) poor initial vapor distribution can reduce contacting efficiency and promote premature flooding. The problem is to evenly distribute the vapor feed laterally before it ascends through the packed bed.

"There are two ways to accomplish proper distribution. In an ordinary fractionating tower which operates at a substantial pressure (25-300 psig), a small amount of pressure drop through a vapor distributor is of no consequence. In this kind of tower an orifice-type vapor distributor with a pressure drop of 8 inches of water (i.e., 0.25 psig) at design vapor rates is sufficient. The basis for this is:

▶ The pressure drop in the packing will rarely exceed two inches of water per foot of packing. A larger pressure drop in the vapor distributor than in the bottom foot of packing will prevent minor obstructions in the lower part of the packed bed from distorting the initial vapor distribution.
▶ At vapor rates of 50% of design, the pressure drop through the orifice-type vapor distributor will still be two inches of water (pressure drop varies with the square of the flow).

"Figure 2-4 shows how a liquid-collector chimney tray doubles as a vapor distributor. When calculating the pressure drop through the chimney, you

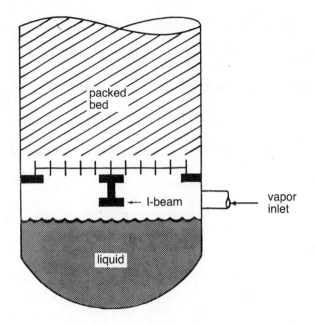

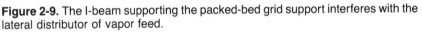

Figure 2-9. The I-beam supporting the packed-bed grid support interferes with the lateral distributor of vapor feed.

can neglect the length of the chimney itself and treat the chimney as a single sharp-edged orifice.

"Obtaining good vapor distribution in a vacuum tower is a more difficult task. Unfortunately, a pressure drop of eight inches of water in a deep vacuum tower is excessive. Also, a commonly overlooked source of trouble is the beams supporting the packing support grid. In a large-diameter tower these I-beams may be quite thick and interfere with the lateral distribution of vapor underneath the packing.

"The process designer must calculate the pressure drop of the vapor as it flows underneath the support grid. This calculation is especially important at the level in which vapor feed is introduced into a column. Figure 2-9 shows an improperly designed tower. Note how the beam will force the vapors to preferentially flow up the right side of the packed bed. In this tower the engineer has two choices to correct this design:

▶ Provide two feed inlets, one on either side of the I-beam.
▶ Leave sufficient space underneath the I-beam so that the calculated pressure drop for half the feed vapors will be less than 10% of the anticipated pressure drop in the packed bed above. The area underneath the I-beam can be treated as a sharp-edged orifice for the purpose of this calculation.

"As the I-beams in a very large-diameter (30-40-feet) vacuum tower may be 1-2 feet thick, the process designer must take this problem into account before setting the vertical dimensions of the column. The large empty area inside low-pressure packed columns is a necessary consequence of using high-capacity packing instead of conventional trays."

Liquid Distribution and Collection

"It rather sounds," said Mr. Hasselback, "that there is quite a bit of expertise required in designing a packed tower. Did that nut from Chicago, who revamped our crude unit, take all the factors into account?"

"I'm afraid not," I responded, "he was more of a theoretical engineer, not one to be overly concerned with details. "And really, that's what corporate headquarters sent me down here to explain to you—that there's nothing wrong with repacking the crude tower, rather than using trays, if we both pay more attention to the details; you on the operational end, and I on the design end.

"By the way, before I head home, there is still one aspect of the problem we have not discussed yet—handling liquids in a packed column."

Liquid Distribution

"In a trayed column there is no serious liquid distribution problem. Once past the top tray, the outlet weirs on each tray effectively provide for the even horizontal flow of liquid across the tray. The vertical component of flow in a downcomer is of no consequence as far as vapor-liquid contacting is concerned.

"In packed towers, just the opposite is true. The packing will do nothing to redistribute the liquid as it flows down the tower. Poor initial liquid distribution will remain poor, and even get worse. If the liquid is poorly distributed, it will not effectively contact the upflowing vapors, and the tower efficiency will suffer. There are two general methods to distribute liquid on top of a packed bed: spray distributors and troughs.

Trough distributor. This kind of device is preferred if the fluid to be distributed is a vapor-liquid mixture or if it contains a lot of particulate matter which can plug the holes in a spray distributor. The disadvantage of a trough distributor is that it must be installed level, because if it slopes an inch or two, substantial liquid maldistribution will result. Also, it requires more vertical tower height to install than a spray distributor.

Spray distributor. Figure 2-10 shows a side view of a spray distributor. Note how the sketch includes external, dual-element filters. Remember that

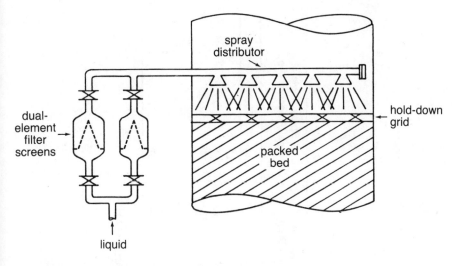

Figure 2-10. A dual-element filter screen will protect the spray nozzles in a liquid distributor from plugging.

a partially plugged spray distributor is worse than no distributor at all. The spray nozzles must be designed so that the spray cones entirely cover the packed bed. The diameter of the spray cone is a function of the height of the spray nozzle above the packed bed, the type of nozzle selected, and the volume of liquid passing through the spray head. Table 2-1 shows the data required to specify the spray headers.[2]

"As the spray header is typically the preferred method of reflux and pumparound return liquid distribution, a few words of caution are pertinent:

▶ The pressure drop in the lateral arms of the spray distributor must be small compared to the pressure drop in the spray headers.

▶ Excessive spray-header pressure drop (more than 30-40 psig) can result in a mist spray, which will reduce the towers fractionation efficiency.

▶ Never imbed the spray distributor in-between packed beds directly in the packing. This is guaranteed to result in premature flooding.

▶ Size the external filter elements with openings slightly smaller than the ports of the spray header. Do not include a by-pass around these filter elements, as one element must always be kept onstream.

▶ Do not oversize spray distributors. You will still want complete liquid wetting of the packed bed at low liquid rates. Remember that the diameter of the spray cone will decrease as liquid rates are reduced. Try your shower at home to prove it.

Table 2-1
Spray Nozzle Sizes

Pipe Connection (Inches)	Orifice Diam. (Inches)	Max. Free Passage (Inches)	Capacity gpm at psi Pressure Drop			Spray Angle at psi Pressure Drop		
			5 psi	10 psi	40 psi	5 psi	10 psi	40 psi
1/4	1/8	1/16	.89	1.2	2.2	114°	120°	120°
1/4	15/64	1/8	2.6	3.5	6.4	114°	120°	121°
3/4	25/64	11/64	5.2	7.0	12.9	115°	120°	121°
1	33/64	7/32	9.5	12.9	24	117°	120°	124°
2	63/64	7/16	41	55	101	120°	124°	125°
3	1 3/8	11/16	82	111	205	120°	125°	125°
4	2	13/16	162	220	405	120°	125°	125°

(Adapted from Fulljet Nozzles Technical Bulletin, p. 12.)

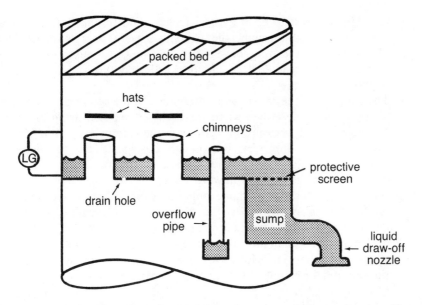

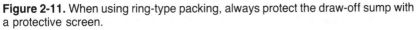

Figure 2-11. When using ring-type packing, always protect the draw-off sump with a protective screen.

Liquid Collection

"The liquid raining down from a packed section is best collected on a chimney tray collection pan as shown in Figure 2-11. This is a total trap-out collection tray in the sense that all the liquid is supposed to be withdrawn from the column. Some important features of this design are:

▶ The sump is shielded from loose rings with a screen. If rings fall into a sump, they will work their way down to the pump which takes suction on the sump. Metal rings which reach a centrifugal pump impeller will damage the pump's seals and bearings. A few rings lying on top of the screen will not interfere with the flow of liquid into the sump. This screen is not supplied by the packing vendor, yet it is a vital component for any tower with ring-type packing. The screen is constructed of common walkway or subway grating. The percent open area is not critical in this service.

▶ The height of the chimneys is set by the required liquid residence time. Normally, one will wish to maintain a liquid level inside the tower, and the volume of liquid inside the sump is insufficient to provide sufficient residence time (typically 1-3 minutes). For very large-diameter towers, the chimneys should be at least 12 inches high. In one 42-foot vacuum tower I crawled through, the chimney's were only 6 inches high. Unfortunately, the tray deck sagged in places to a depth of 8 inches. Obviously, a great deal of liquid overflowed this tray through the depressed chimneys.

▶ The diameter of the chimneys is determined by the need for proper vapor distribution, as described when we discussed vapor distributor design. Note that a high pressure drop through the chimneys will *not* result in tower flooding. However, the process designer needs to advise the mechanical designer to provide adequate structural strength in the chimney to withstand this upward force.

▶ The "hats," which keep liquid from raining down through the chimneys, must be set high enough above the chimney to avoid creating a substantial pressure drop. I have frequently found these hats blown off because the designer placed them too close to the top of the chimney and a pressure surge ripped them loose from the chimneys. The peripheral area between the hats and the chimneys should be at least twice the cross-sectional area of the chimneys.

▶ The *overflow pipe* will prevent liquid from interfering with vapor flow by flowing down the chimneys. If a high liquid level occurs on the tray due to a level control problem, the liquid will overflow into the chimneys. This promotes entrainment and can cause premature flooding of the packed bed above the tray. Note that the overflow pipe is liquid-sealed at the bottom to prevent vapor from blowing up through it.

▶ The draw-off nozzle is located flush with the bottom of the sump. Several ½ of an inch drain holes are provided on the tray decks. These features are necessary to allow the tray to be drained on unit shutdown and dehydrated on start-up. Drain holes in the sump are not necessary and will cause excessive leakage during normal operation."

The sun was setting behind the crude unit as I drove out of the refinery. Back in Chicago I heard that, after my departure, Mr. Hasselback had phoned the Vice-President and told him it wouldn't be necessary to send any more crazy Yankees down to see him. I think that could have been a compliment.

References

1. Koch Engineering Co., FLEXIPAC® Bulletin KFP-Z, January 1979. Figure 8c. Pressure drop for Type 3 FLEXIPAC®.

2. Fulljet Nozzles Technical Bulletin, spray nozzle sizes, p. 12.

3

Vacuum Tower Design

Anyone who has ever seen crude oil distilled in the lab under atmospheric pressure will appreciate the importance of a vacuum tower. At about 680-700°F, the residual liquid will give off yellowish vapor. This is a manifestation of the thermal cracking that degrades the quality of virgin distillates and gas oils.

The vacuum tower distills most of the gas oil out of crude while still avoiding excessive temperatures. The crude unit's primary tower is intended to fractionate between naphtha, kerosene, and furnace oil. The vacuum tower only has one function: to produce a clean, high-boiling gas oil suitable for cracking-plant or lube-oils refining feed.

A vacuum tower's flash zone typically operates at 1-2 psia and 720-780°F. The tower is designed to tolerate a small degree of thermal cracking. A sketch of a typical vacuum tower is shown in Figure 3-1.

There are three main sections in a vacuum tower: (1) the wash-oil section, (2) the heavy gas-oil pumparound, and (3) the light-vacuum, gas-oil pumparound. Both pumparound circuits are used to remove heat from the tower and condense the upflowing vapors. As shown in Figure 3-1, both light and heavy gas-oil streams are combined outside the column.

Wash-Oil Section Design

The purpose of the wash-oil section is to de-entrain residual liquid from vapors rising from the flash zone. The tar in these vapors will contaminate the heavy gas-oil product with nickel, vanadium, and Conradson carbon. These impurities will ruin the gas oil for further processing in a fluid catalytic cracker or heavy-oils plant.

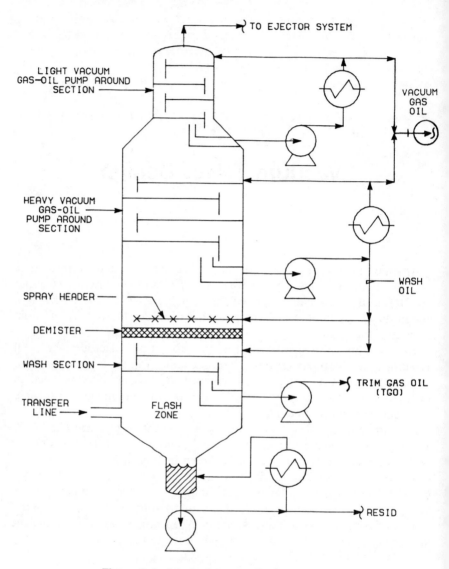

Figure 3-1. A typical vacuum tower.

The objectives in cleaning the flash-zone vapors are to do so with as little liquid reflux (i.e., wash oil) as possible, a minimum of pressure drop, and without coking the wash-oil section.

In modern vacuum tower design the wash-oil section is almost invariably a packed section sprayed with heavy-vacuum gas oil. The minimum amount of liquid required to completely wet the top of a packed bed is 0.3 gpm per square foot of bed surface. One ought to have about one spray nozzle for each five square feet. The bottom tip of the spray nozzle should be at least two feet above the top of the packing, and the total height required for the spray assembly will be about one foot.

Two practical points which the designer should remember are:

▶ Always insist that the spray assembly be assembled outside the tower and tested with water for proper distribution. The wash-oil packing will coke up in any nonwetted areas.

▶ Provide adequate height (about two feet) between the top of the spray headers and the bottom heavy-vacuum, gas-oil draw-off pan for an inspector to crawl into the tower and approve the final spray-header installation.

The rationale for packing rather than trays in the wash section is based on the lower pressure-drop characteristics of packing. About three or four feet of packing will do an excellent job of cleaning up the flash-zone vapors if the packing is evenly wetted. The proper quantity of wash oil and its even distribution are far more important than the type or depth of packing in preventing entrainment.

The author has a strong prejudice against the use of ring-type packing in the wash-oil sections of vacuum towers. The rings migrate through the packing support and wind up in the suction strainer of the bottoms pump. A grid- or mesh-type packing is far more likely to stay put. Figure 3-2 shows one type of rugged, high-capacity packing.

If rings are selected for wash-section packing service, a bar screen in the bottom of the vacuum tower is absolutely essential to protect the vacuum bottoms pumps from sucking in stray rings. A bar-screen design is shown in Figure 3-3. The horizontal dimensions betwen the bars will be a function of the size of the rings.

Most of the wash oil will evaporate in the wash-section packing. This is determined by heat-balance calculations. Typically one-third of the wash oil will not evaporate. There is usually one volume of entrained liquid for each two volumes of residual wash oil. This combined liquid stream is recycled back to the vacuum heater for reevaporation of the wash oil.

Flash-Zone Temperature

Vacuum units are operated at the maximum flash-zone temperature consistent with minimum cracking. This temperature is determined empirically by the unit operators when they observe a sudden loss in vacuum as they raise the heater outlet temperature past a certain point. Above this

Figure 3-2. Glitsch Grid®—a rugged, high-capacity packing for vacuum service. (Courtesy F.W. Glitsch Co., Inc.)

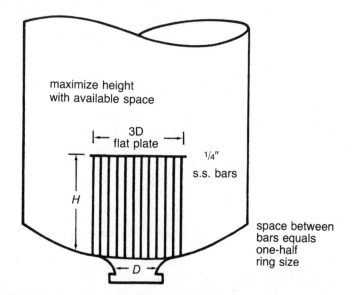

maximize height
with available space

3D
flat plate

¼″
s.s. bars

H

space between
bars equals
one-half
ring size

D

Figure 3-3. A bar screen over the bottom nozzle is required if rings are to be used in a packed vacuum tower.

temperature, the rapid evolution of cracked gas overloads the overhead ejector system.

This critical point is between 750 and 800°F heater outlet (the flash-zone temperature is normally 20°F lower than the heater outlet). It is a function of heater design and feed stock characteristics. The more paraffinic the feed, the lower the critical flash-zone temperature.

If a unit is to operate at flash-zone temperatures above 730°F, it will be necessary to quench the liquid in the bottom of the tower. Also, the residence time of liquid should be kept to a few minutes. Both these steps are necessary to prevent thermal cracking in the bottom boot. Figure 3-4 shows how the bottoms stream is recirculated through an external cooler to remove heat from the bottom's boot.

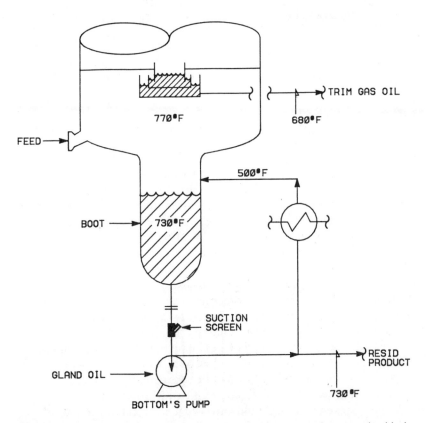

Figure 3-4. The liquid in the bottom of a vacuum tower must be quenched below the flash-zone temperature.

Pumparound Design

The heavy-vacuum gas-oil and light-vacuum gas-oil pumparound circuits are usually designed to remove heat in a 2:1 ratio. The vacuum tower diameter will be set by the heavy-vacuum gas-oil pumparound section. Hence, high-capacity, low pressure-drop packing is almost always used in this section.

In most vacuum towers there is no attempt to fractionate between light- and heavy-vacuum gas oil. It is assumed that both streams are best combined and charged to cracker feed. However, in every vacuum column I have observed the light-vacuum gas oil contained a surprising amount of material in the diesel oil boiling range.

Light-Vacuum Gas-Oil Distillation

Volume % Off	Temperature (°F)
0	400
10	490
30	530
50	600
70	650
90	675
100	750

Note that if the last 10% of the light-vacuum gas oil was removed, the remaining stream would be suitable for sale as diesel oil. To accomplish this objective, one refinery installed a fractionation zone in the conical section of their vacuum tower, between the light and heavy gas-oil pumparound section. Figure 3-5 illustrates the modification.

Some important features of this design are:

▶ Hot, light-vacuum gas oil is used for reflux. If cold reflux is used, only half as much is required, and it becomes more difficult to distribute the reflux evenly across the top of the diesel oil fractionation section.

▶ About one volume of reflux is required for each four volumes of diesel oil produced. The liquid from the diesel oil section will simply drain into the heavy-vacuum gas-oil pumparound section. The draw temperature of the heavy-vacuum gas oil will not be particularly affected, but the light-vacuum gas-oil draw temperature will drop about 50°F.

▶ The new packed section should have two theoretical fractionation stages. This will require three valve-type trays or about six feet of packing. This section will then have a pressure drop of 6-8 mm Hg.

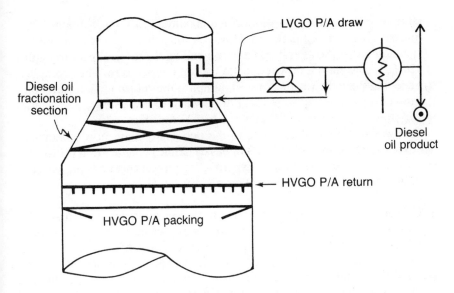

Figure 3-5. Inserting a fractionation zone in a vacuum tower can permit production of a diesel oil product.

This pressure drop will be additive to the flash-zone pressure and hence will reduce vaporization in the flash-zone section and retard ultimate gas-oil recovery. This debit has to be compared against the incentive to recover diesel oil from cracker gas-oil feed. For the particular installation shown in Figure 3-5, 25% of the gas-oil production was diverted to the refinery diesel oil pool.

The configuration of the light-vacuum gas-oil pumparound section will largely depend on the vacuum tower top temperature selected. This subject can be extremely complex, as illustrated by the following section.

Tower Top Temperature

There is a widespread belief among operating personnel that many process design engineers are not quite sure as to how process equipment reacts in the field. The subject of optimum vacuum unit tower top pressure is a case in point.

The principle of vacuum unit operation is to minimize pressure. The lower the vapor load to the ejector overhead system, the more vacuum the jets can draw and hence the lower the tower pressure. It follows, then, that one should design for a minimum tower top temperature to reduce the pounds of light hydrocarbon vapors that flash overhead from the vacuum tower into the ejector system.

Until recently, I never questioned that maximum vacuum is obtained by a minimum tower top temperature. However, on a visit to a vacuum unit last year, I noted that the operators were controlling the tower top temperature at 320°F. I insisted that they reduce tower top temperature. They complied by reducing the light-vacuum gas-oil pumparound return temperature, and the tower top temperature fell to 190°F. Much to my dismay, the vacuum tower pressure rose from 90 mm Hg to 120 mm Hg!

This was terribly embarrassing to me personally and, more important, appeared to contradict my beliefs in basic chemical engineering principles. However, after several days of experimentation on this unit and another vacuum tower, I came to the following conclusions:

▶ On vacuum units where there is no precondenser ahead of the first-stage jet, minimum tower top temperature always results in the best vacuum.
▶ On vacuum units which have a precondenser ahead of the first-stage jet, the optimum tower top temperature is between 250°F and 350°F.
▶ On dry vacuum units, which have no precondenser, it is necessary to raise the tower top temperature to obtain the best vacuum whenever the steam to the first-stage jet is shut off.

The reason for this odd behavior is that the increased light hydrocarbons that escape from the top of a vacuum unit as the temperature increases change the equilibrium flash in the precondenser. The light hydrocarbons absorb gas and therefore decrease the vapor load to the first-stage jets. The optimum tower top temperature is not reached until the outlet temperature of the precondenser starts increasing due to higher heat duty. This effect is shown qualitatively in Figure 3-6.

Wet Versus Dry Towers

At the conception of any vacuum tower design, the process engineer must decide if the tower will be a wet or dry tower.

For a wet tower velocity steam will be injected into the vacuum heater tube passes. Also, stripping steam will be used in a trayed stripping section located below the flash section. The velocity steam will enhance vaporization in the heater tubes, while the stripping steam (if 0.2 pounds of steam per gallon of bottoms is used) will vaporize 12–18% of the flash-zone liquid across the bottom stripping trays. A wet vacuum tower must always have a precondenser (see Figure 3-7) on the vacuum tower overhead system. A precondenser is required to condense the velocity stripping steam from the tail gas ahead of the first-stage ejector.

A dry vacuum tower will not use any steam. It will not have a bottoms steam stripping section, nor will velocity steam be used in the heater coils (of

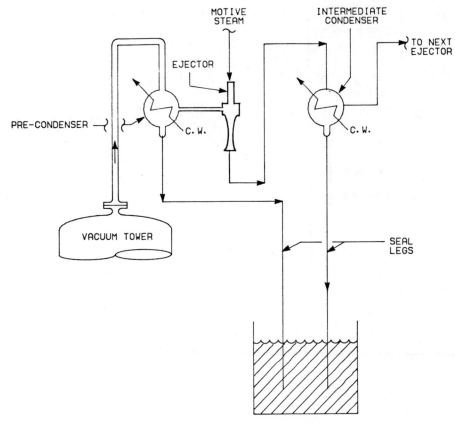

Figure 3-6. A minimum tower top temperature is only optimum when the ejector system does not have a precondenser.

course, steam must still be connected to each heater coil for use in steaming out the tubes during an emergency). Surprisingly, a dry vacuum tower can obtain the same degree of vaporization as a wet tower. The reason for this apparent anomaly is that a dry tower typically operates with a flash-zone pressure of 30 mm Hg, whereas the corresponding value for a wet tower is 90 mm Hg. (See Figure 3-8 for a typical vaporization chart showing the effect of flash-zone pressure on percent vaporized.)

The wet vacuum tower achieves a high degree of vaporization as the hydrocarbon partial pressure is lowered. The dry tower runs at a low absolute pressure. Why, then, don't we combine stripping steam with the low pressures obtainable in dry vacuum towers and hence design a supervaporizer vacuum unit?

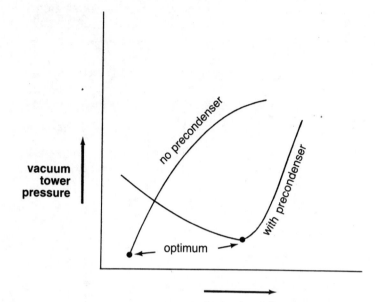

Figure 3-7. A wet vacuum tower must always have a precondenser in the overhead system.

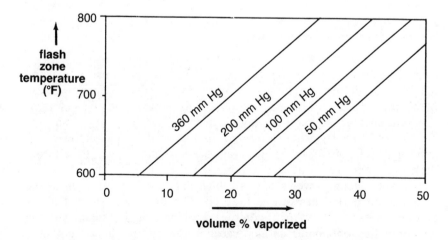

Figure 3-8. A typical vaporization curve for a vacuum unit.

The answer is that a low flash-zone pressure cannot, in practice, be obtained in a wet vacuum unit. Remember that a wet vacuum unit must have a precondenser, as shown in Figure 3-7. Let us assume that this precondenser runs at a minimum outlet temperature of 110°F. At this temperature, the vapor pressure of water is 65 mm Hg. Neglecting the other factors that contribute to the vacuum tower top pressure (i.e., hydrocarbon partial pressure and pressure drop through the precondenser), the minimum tower top pressure is then 65 mm Hg.

In practice, this means that the minimum flash-zone pressure is 90 mm Hg. If the mole percent steam in the flash zone is 60-70%, the hydrocarbon partial pressure in the flash zone will be about 30 mm Hg

$$HC_{pp} = P_t (1.00 - M_s)$$

where:
HC_{pp} = hydrocarbon partial pressure, mm Hg.
P_t = total pressure, mm Hg.
M_s = mole fraction steam in flash zone.

Based on one rather detailed study, I have drawn the following conclusions as to the selection of dry versus wet vacuum towers:

▶ Approximately the same degree of vaporization can be obtained in either tower.
▶ The diameter of the dry tower will be about the same as the wet tower. The larger volume of vapor generated in the low-pressure dry tower will be balanced by the extra moles of steam in the wet tower.
▶ The steam consumption in the dry tower will actually be slightly higher than in the wet tower. This seeming contradiction is due to the very large steam demand for the first-stage jets in the dry tower.

Considering all factors, a dry tower is somewhat more cost effective than a wet tower. The dry tower will not need the large precondensers shown in Figure 3-7. Also, the bottoms trayed steam-stripping section can be dispensed with. From a practical operating point of view, the dry tower is also preferred because there is no possibility of getting slugs of water into the tower with the bottoms stripping steam. I have frequently seen the bottom trays in a wet vacuum tower dislodged by wet stripping steam.

4

Trayed Tower Internals

There is more to designing fractionation columns than specifying the number and type of trays or packing required. In particular, the withdrawal of liquid products from the tower and the return of reflux streams to the tower present a number of practical design difficulties. An experience I had on a wax fractionator is representative of such problems.

The wax fractionator was used to separate different boiling-point waxes derived from petroleum gas oils. The tower had recently been retrayed to expand its capacity. On start-up, the operators discovered that the tower no longer performed properly. Clean, middle boiling-point wax could not be withdrawn from the center of the fractionator.

A careful review of the tower internal drawings and discussions with plant operating personnel revealed that two design errors had been made.

Avoid Internal Level Connections

When the process designer laid out the new tray configuration, he rotated the tower top tray by 90° to facilitate liquid reflux distribution on the top tray. As a result, all the trays in the tower were installed at right angles to their original orientation. When the designer specified the layout for the middle wax draw-off sump (see Figure 4-1), he realized that the existing level-gauge taps and draw-off nozzle were 90° out of alignment with the new sump. His solution to the problem was simple: connect the existing nozzles to the new sump with internal piping.

The internal level-gauge piping shown in Figure 4-1 consisted of three-quarter-inch piping with several elbows. It is difficult enough to keep level taps clear of obstructions when they are directly connected to a reservoir of liquid with short, straight lines. Using long lines with elbows makes it almost impossible to clear obstructions from the level taps, especially when the lines cannot be cleaned because they are inside an operating tower.

Because the taps to the level gauge were plugged, the operators could not determine the liquid level in the draw-off sump. Therefore, they could not know if the sump was overflowing with wax or empty.

The Dangers of Internal Draw-Off

Anyone who has seen flanged piping assembled in the field realizes that the sections of pipe frequently do not mate exactly. Often a bad fit is not revealed until the piping is pressure-tested for leaks. Also, a flange which may be tight when cold, starts leaking upon exposure to thermal stress.

Figure 4-1 shows that a leaking flange was actually the cause of the inability to draw-off middle boiling-point wax from the fractionator. The tower was shutdown and opened for inspection. Inside the flange connecting the bottom of the draw-off sump to the internal draw-off line was cocked by ¼ of an inch. This small opening was sufficient for the wax product to leak through, thus depriving the draw-off nozzle of liquid flow.

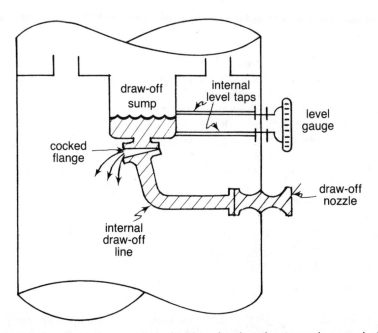

Figure 4-1. Locating process piping inside a fractionation tower is poor design practice.

Overflowing Draw-Off Sumps

A lube-oil prefractionating tower was limited to 200 gpm of 30-weight oil that could be drawn-off the side of the column. The draw-off pan was clearly overflowing, indicating that there was plenty of liquid available. The rundown line was twice the diameter needed for a small friction loss in the piping so that there was plenty of hydraulic head available. The problem persisted for a decade—ever since the fractionator was commissioned. Figure 4-2 explains the design error.

Note that both a gate valve and a control valve are located on the horizontal run of pipe between the draw-off nozzle and the first elbow turning down. At a flow of 200 gpm, the calculated pressure loss through both valves is 0.5 psig. As the tank that the 30-weight oil ran down to was 20 psig below the pressure of the tower, could the small pressure loss through the valves be considered as inconsequential? The answer is NO!

The hydraulic driving force available to push the oil out of the tower is only the liquid head above the centerline of the draw-off nozzle. This dimension is designated as H in Figure 4-2. The oil withdrawn from the tower had a specific gravity of 0.80. The 0.5 psig head loss in the external piping equals a liquid head loss of 18 inches:

$$\text{head loss (inches of liquid)} = \frac{0.5 \text{ psig} \times 28 \text{ inches water}}{0.80 \text{ sp gr}} = 18 \text{ inches}$$

The length of H in Figure 4-2 is 18 inches.

The correct way to design the fractionator tower side draw-off piping is to locate valves downstream of a long (5-10 feet) vertical run of pipe. The first fitting connected to the draw-off nozzle must be a 90° elbow turning down. Assuming that this elbow is the same diameter as the draw-off nozzle, the minimum height for H between the centerline of the draw-off nozzle and the maximum height of liquid on the draw-off pan is calculated as follows:

$$H = 15 \times 10^{-6} \times G^2/D^4$$

where:
H = theoretical head, inches.
G = hot-liquid discharge, gph.
D = ID of nozzle, inches.

If G is based on a normal expected flow of product, the calculated value for H should be doubled. This will allow for fluctuations in production rate as well as minor restrictions due to fouling in the draw-off nozzle.

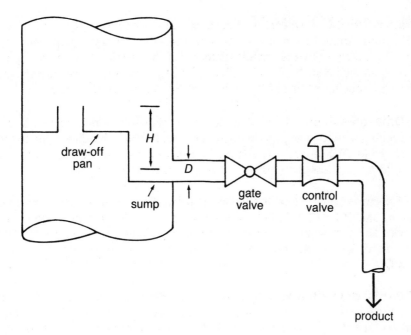

Figure 4-2. Locating valves on a draw-off line before the piping descends will cause the draw-off pan to overflow.

Coordinating Nozzle Location with Tray Design

Most fractionating tower trays are designed and fabricated by three vendors. Although each markets a somewhat unique valve tray, the overall capacity and efficiency of their trays are not, in my experience, particularly different. Each of these vendors will do a professional job of designing the tower internals that support the operation of their equipment. It is up to the process design engineer to allocate adequate vessel height to permit the valve tray vendor to fit the required internals into the tower. The following tabulation represents the minimum heights to be used and nozzle location relative to the vertical position of the trays.

Seal pans. Normally a downcomer is sealed in the liquid of the tray the downcomer empties onto. For the bottom tray, a small seal pan (provided by the tray vendor) is required. This seal pan is located one tray space plus six inches below the bottom tray.

Feed nozzles. An intermediate feed stream or a pumparound return should be introduced six inches above the lower tray (as measured from the bottom of the feed distributor pipe). The nozzle should be as close as practical to the downcomer. For a mixed vapor-liquid feed, the feed distributor should be midway between the adjacent trays, with the tray spacing increased by the outside diameter of the nozzle. Also, if the top of the liquid feed distributor is less than half a tray spacing to the tray above, the tray spacing must also be increased by the nozzle diameter.

Draw-off sumps. The formula for sizing draw-off sumps is given in the preceding section. The process engineer should specify this dimension to the tray vendor. The space between the bottom of the sump and the tray below should be not less than 80% of the normal tray spacing.

Thermosiphon reboiler vapor return. The center or reboiler return nozzle should be 12 inches plus one normal tray space below the bottom tray deck. The nozzle should enter the tower parallel with the seal pan. The bottom of the nozzle should be 12 inches above the maximum high liquid level.

Partial draw-offs. While no draw-off pan should ever be designed that cannot overflow, some draw-offs are intended to be total draw-offs, and others are designed to be partial draw-offs. Withdrawing 50% of the downflowing liquid as product and permitting the remainder to cascade down the tower as reflux requires a partial draw-off tray. The required vertical height for installation of a partial draw-off tray is one normal tray space plus two inches plus the diameter of the draw-off nozzle.

Draw-off sumps can, and frequently are, built into a recessed area of the lower tray. This practice lowers vertical tower height. However, it reduces the fractionation efficiency of the tower by reducing vapor-liquid disengagement volume between trays.

Never introduce a feed, reflux, or pumparound stream into a downcomer. Even if, in theory, it is impossible to have vapor in a stream, in practice an exchanger may leak and inject vapor into the stream. Charging vapor into a downcomer will cause premature flooding of the tray above.

Feed and Reflux Distributors

Initial feed distribution in a trayed tower is not as vital as in a packed column. Poorly distributed liquid feed in a packed tower simply stays maldistributed regardless of the depth of packing.

On the other hand, the top tray of a fractionator acts as an excellent liquid distributor, whereas the bottom tray is a perfect vapor distributor. Therefore, sophisticated and expensive feed distributors for sections of towers with 15 or 20 trays are not worthwhile.

For sections of just three or four trays, proper liquid distribution is vital. As an example, plant test data on one pumparound section showed that the efficiency of the top tray was halved when its liquid distributor was removed.

A slotted or perforated pipe makes an acceptable liquid distributor. The openings should be designed to produce a pressure drop of about five times the pressure drop in the distributor pipe. The openings should be on the bottom of the pipe. The minimum pressure drop through these openings should be 1-2 psi; the maximum should be 15-20 psi. Greater pressure drops than this amount will promote mist formation of the liquid feed.

Hot liquid or vapor feeds should not be discharged against (and certainly not into) downcomers, as the resulting boiling inside the downcomers can cause premature flooding of the column.

A mixed-phase distributor should follow the same design criteria as a liquid distributor. The holes on the bottom of the pipe are sized for the liquid portion of the feed, while the vapor in the feed is used to size the holes in the top of the pipe.

A totally vaporized feed does not require any distributor. The tray above the vapor feed is in itself a vapor distributor. Again, do not discharge the vapor against a downcomer. If a level tap is located directly across the tower from the vapor inlet nozzle, an impingement plate in front of the nozzle is a good idea.

Never Seal a Downcomer

In a small coastal refinery in Georgia, a tower employed in the manufacture of asphalt from Mexican crude oil was retrayed. The objective was to increase capacity, but the result was a severe reduction in fractionation efficiency. A serious error, illustrated in Figure 4-3, was made in the revamp of the column.

The downcomer from the bottom tray was converted to a draw-off box. The product draw-off nozzle was used to drain this box. Note that the draw-off box had no provision for overflow. Whenever the product flow was interrupted, liquid would back-up out of the downcomer and flood the bottom tray. This, in turn, would lead to the flooding of the entire fractionator.

By employing an enclosed box, the designer intended to maximize liquid production from the condensed vapors. However, as there was no way for the bottom tray to overflow internally in the tower, a reduction in the liquid draw-off rate caused the tower to fill with liquid and ruin the fractionation.

Actually, this particular error might have escaped management notice if the designer had not compounded his mistake with a second error.

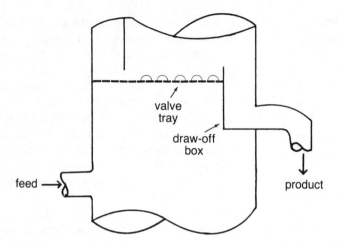

Figure 4-3. Never totally enclose the bottom of a downcomer.

Side-Stream Steam-Stripper Hydraulics

Figure 4-4 shows a properly designed steam stripper serving a fractionation column. Note how the downcomer discharges into a seal plan, which then overflows into a total trap-out pan. The liquid withdrawn from the trap-out pan flows by gravity into the stripper. Naturally, the liquid inlet to the stripper must be below the draw-off nozzle on the fractionator. The minimum distance for this elevation is

$$E = P_L + \left(\frac{2.31}{\text{sp gr}}\right) \times (P_V)$$

where:

E = the minimum elevation between the draw-off nozzle and the stripper inlet, feet.

P_L = pressure drop due to friction in the liquid inlet piping, feet of liquid.

sp gr = specific gravity of liquid at the process temperature.

P_V = pressure drop due to friction in the vapor line (including nozzle exit and entrance losses), psi.

For the asphaltic crude unit in Georgia, the designer specified a 2-inch stripper overhead vapor line. This line was far too small for the available elevation. Thus, whenever stripping steam was introduced to the side-stream stripper, the P_V term in the previous equation became excessive.

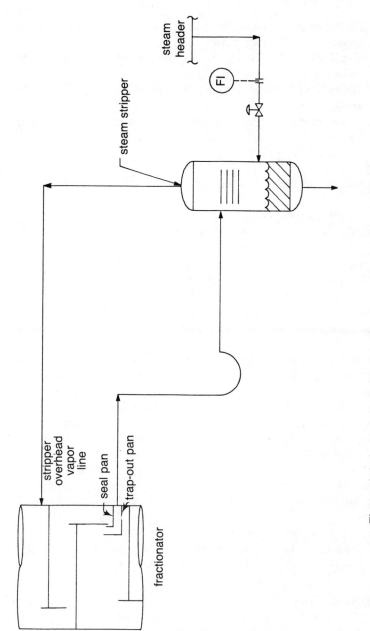

Figure 4-4. A properly sized vapor line is needed to prevent the draw-off.

The following sequence of events was then initiated:

1. The pressure in the stripper increased and prevented the downflow of liquid from the fractionator.
2. The draw-off box in Figure 4-4 filled and backed-up onto the bottom valve tray.
3. The entire fractionator flooded and the separation efficiency of the tower went down.
4. The plant manager telephoned the engineering office in Chicago to make appropriate comments pertaining to the ancestry of Yankees in general and design engineers in particular.

Combination Pumparound Draw-Off and Product Trap-Out Pan

If often transpires that a fractionation tower internal is required that will simultaneously serve the following functions:

▶ Totally trap-out all the downflowing liquid.
▶ Provide a reservoir for a circulating pumparound stream.
▶ Draw-off the total excess liquid condensed by the pumparound stream to a side stripper. Flow to be by gravity.

Figure 4-5 summarizes a novel method used on several towers which had these requirements. The flow to the steam stripper was controlled by liquid overflowing the dam on the trap-out tray. The liquid level in the pumparound reservoir was set by the height of the dam. This arrangement saves the need for a control valve in the liquid feed line to the stripper. Also, the required liquid volume for the pumparound reservoir is greatly reduced as the reservoir level never varies by more than a few inches, that is, the level may never fall below the height of the dam.

Incidentally, the "loop seal" shown on the liquid line between the fractionator and the stripper is necessary to prevent stripping steam from backing-up the liquid line, instead of flowing out the vapor line. If the stripping steam did enter the liquid line, the draw-off pan could not drain properly and would overflow.

The loop seal is typically located near the stripper and is 2-3 feet high. For strippers that are fed from a pump, a loop seal is unnecessary.

Leak-Proofing Draw-Off Pans

If total draw-off of liquid is required in a tower, a total trap-out chimney tray or a draw-off pan is needed. A practical problem with such pans is that they can leak due to imperfect assembly. The leakage is compounded by the

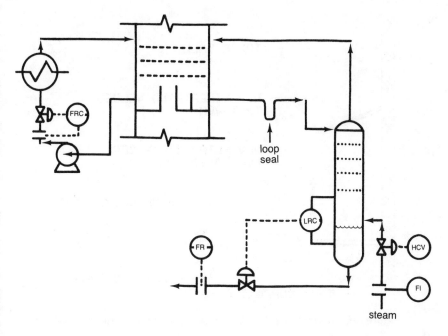

loop
seal

Figure 4-5. Holding the level on a pumparound draw-off pan can be facilitated by getting the net product to overflow a dam.

substantial head of liquid required to force the fluid through the draw-off nozzle.

An excellent method successfully employed many times is detailed in Figure 4-6. First, the tray deck sections, after being assembled inside the tower, are seal-welded together. Second, to stop leakage at the tray support ring, a strip is welded onto the periphery of the tray. The strip is located about 2 inches from the vessel wall, and its height is the same as the overflow weir. A wiper ring is installed above the peripheral strip. The ring is 2½ inches wide.

This type of installation is especially useful in large-diameter towers with low rates of liquid traffic.

Reviewing Vendor Tray Drawings

Among the purveyors of process equipment, tray vendors are probably the most reliable. Hence, a detailed review of mechanical and construction drawings is not mandatory.

One should check that the vendor tray elevations correspond to the nozzles being provided by the vessel fabricator. Remember that the tray

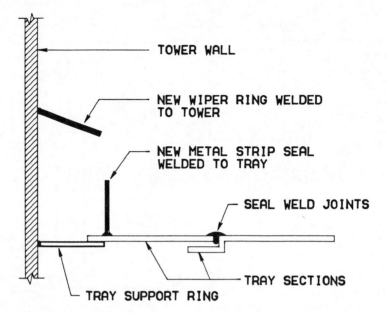

Figure 4-6. Strategic welding on a valve draw-off tray will stop leaks.

manufacturer does not build the tower in which the trays will be installed. Watch out for tray orientations that do not match up with the vessel nozzle orientation. One common error is to locate level taps in the vessel wall that are not lined up with the draw-off sump.

In practice, many major fractionators are *not* properly assembled in the field. It is a long way from the designers penciled vessel sketch to tower field assembly. From experience, I have found it essential to crawl through and inspect trayed towers before the final manway is bolted down. I have had many opportunities to regret the occasions when I neglected to take this precaution.

References

1. Koch Engineering Company, Inc., *FLEXITRAY® Design Manual*, Bulletin 960-1, 1982.
2. Branan, C., *The Process Engineer's Pocket Handbook,* Gulf Publishing Company, Houston, Texas, 1976.

5

Washing Flash-Zone Vapors

One of the most troublesome areas in many refinery heavy-oil fractionation towers is the wash-oil section (see Figure 5-1). Located directly above the inlet nozzle, the wash-oil section is more vulnerable to coke deposition than any other level in a tower. Also, pressure surges due to slugs of water in the tower's feed (usually on start-up) are most damaging to wash-oil section internals. The common refinery processes that have wash-oil sections are:

▶ Crude atmospheric fractionators
▶ Vacuum towers
▶ Visbreaker fractionators
▶ Coker combination towers
▶ Fluid-cracking unit main columns

Unlike other parts of a column, the wash-oil section is not intended to fractionate. Its function is to de-entrain resid from the upflowing vapors and, if necessary, to desuperheat these vapors.

A well-designed wash-oil section will have the following characteristics.

High capacity. The vapor rate through the wash-oil section is normally the highest in the tower. In some applications, such as in fluid catalytic cracking, the highly superheated vapor feed causes the wash-oil section tower loadings to be double that of other sections of the tower.

Rugged construction. Experienced refinery operators are not surprised to open a tower and find that the wash-oil section trays have been upended. A pressure surge originating in the flash zone or tower bottoms will be most damaging to the wash-oil section.

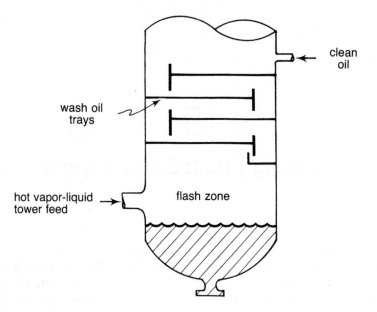

Figure 5-1. The purpose of the wash oil section is to remove entrained black resid from the flash-zone vapors.

Tolerance to coking. Exposed to vapor temperatures of up to 1000°F, the wash-oil section will eventually coke up. The rate of coking will be a function of how well the wash-oil liquid is distributed, the amount of wash oil used, and the temperature and composition of the upflowing vapors. The degree of resid entrainment is also an important variable affecting the rate of coke accumulation.

Choice of Wash-Oil Internals

As I have designed coker combination towers, atmospheric and vacuum crude fractionators, and a fluid-cracking unit main column, I have had plenty of opportunity to try out various wash-oil section internals. With one notable exception, the results have been a disappointment.

Bubble-cap trays. With proper liquid circulation, these trays do an excellent job of washing entrained resid out of the flash-zone vapors. As long as the bubble caps are submerged with cool wash oil, they do not coke very rapidly. However, bubble-cap trays are inherently a low-capacity, vapor-liquid contacting device. Typically, 2-4 bubble-cap trays are used in a wash-oil section.

Valve trays. Not recommended for wash-oil service. The valves or caps will coke and stick to the tray deck.

Shed decks or side-to-side baffles. With a high capacity and good tolerance to coke accumulation, baffles are frequently used in the wash-oil section of delayed cokers- and fluid-cracking units. The main disadvantage of baffles lies in their inability to bring the dirty vapors and clean wash oil into intimate contact. To compensate for this inefficiency, 6-8 sets (levels) of baffles are required in wash-oil service.

Demisters. A mesh pad is an effective de-entrainment device. However, relatively small amounts of coke will cause a high pressure drop through a demister. Consistant and thorough wetting with wash oil is mandatory if a demister pad is used.

Ring packing. Based on many disappointments, I most strongly recommend that rings not be used in wash-oil sections of low-pressure, large-diameter towers. Sooner or later the rings will wind up in the bottom of the tower. A small (1-foot across) hole in the packing support grid will allow 95% of the rings in a 20-foot diameter wash-oil section to drop into the tower bottoms. The chances of damaging the wash-oil section packing support grid due to pressure surges—especially from slugs of water in feed on start-up—are great. The effects of pressure surges are amplified in a low-pressure tower.

Wash-Oil Grid

On two occasions, I had the opportunity to replace existing wash-oil sections with the grid-type packing shown in Figure 5-2. This material proved to have excellent resistance to plugging from coke formation. Also, its mechanical integrity in the face of severe pressure shocks was quite remarkable. Most significant of all, the grid demonstrated a capacity in excess of any other vapor-liquid fractionating column contacting device (with the exception of side-to-side baffles) that I have ever used. For example, the observed vapor and liquid loads in the slurry-oil pumparound or wash-oil section of a fluid-cracking unit column were:

Vapor
1,800,000 lbs/hr
0.55 lbs/ft^3
3,300,000 ft^3/hr
127 molecular weight

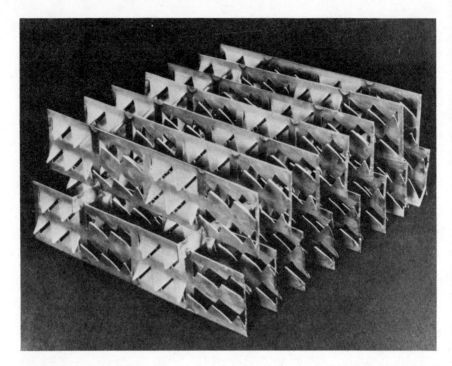

Figure 5-2. A FLEXIGRID™-type material is preferred for a wash-oil section. (Courtesy of Koch Engineering Company, Inc. Koch Engineering Company, Inc. manufactures various equipment under the FLEXITRAY®, FLEXIGRID™, and FLEXIPAC® trademarks. FLEXIPAC® elements are manufactured by Koch Engineering Company, Inc. under exclusive license of Sulzer Brothers Ltd., for the U.S.A., Canada, and Mexico.)

Liquid
  1,900,000 lbs/hr
    5,500 gpm

These data were obtained for a 14-foot diameter tower. At rates slightly above those tabulated, the grid section was observed to flood.

For wash-oil service in a visbreaker fractionator, four feet of grid proved to be quite adequate. The fluid-cracking unit slurry-oil pumparound section had 12 feet of grid, but this amount seemed to be excessive.

The major drawback of the grid proved to be the near impossibility of decoking it during a turnaround. In practice, the grid was discarded and replaced with new sections rather than clean the old coked sections.

6

Distillation Column Internals
for Maximum Flexibility

One of the process engineers' most frequent assignments is to expand the capacity of light hydrocarbon distillation towers. Excluding pumping limitations, which are easily rectified, a distillation tower may be limited by:

▶ Reboiler capacity
▶ Condensing capacity
▶ Tower capacity

There are a number of standard methods, and a greater number of common pitfalls, available to overcome these limitations.

Tower Capacity

A limit on tower capacity manifests itself when the tower floods or when fractionation efficiency declines at higher feed rates.

On an operating tower, the degree of separation between the overhead and bottom products will normally increase as the reflux rate is raised at constant feed rates. If fractionation efficiency declines as the reflux rate is increased, it means that the rate of liquid entrainment in the upflowing vapors has become excessive because the vapor velocity up the tower is too high. This phenomenon is called *jet* or *vapor* flooding.

Liquid flooding is more easily recognized in a tower. The level in the reflux drum (or overhead accumulator) will suddenly rise, while the tower's bottom level falls. The tower top temperature will greatly increase, with the bottom temperature holding constant. In such cases the unvaporized contents of the tower are simply flooding overhead. A sample drawn from the overhead vapor line will contain liquid. The cause of liquid flooding is

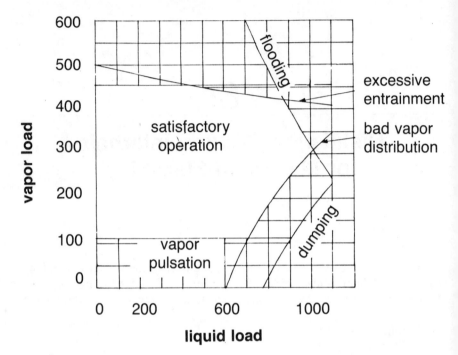

Figure 6-1. A typical performance chart for a distillation column.

the inability of the tower to permit sufficient downflow liquid rates to keep up with the feed and reflux rates.

A high vapor velocity can precipitate liquid flood; a high liquid rate will promote jet flooding. Figure 6-1 shows a typical performance chart for a distillation tower. The area of the chart above the "excessive entrainment" line is the jet-flood region. The area to the right of the "flooding" line is the liquid-flooding region.

Trayed Towers

Figure 6-2 shows a simplified sketch of a section of a trayed tower. Liquid flows across the tray deck, cascades over the weir, and flows through the downcomer onto the next tray deck. Upflowing vapors pass through specially designed openings in the tray deck. There are dozens of proprietary designs for these openings. One of the more common designs is the "valve-type" opening. A picture of a completely assembled valve tray is shown in Figure 6-3.

The simplest way to expand a trayed tower's capacity is to lower the weir. The top edge of the weir can usually be lowered one-quarter to one-half inch below the bottom edge of the opposite downcomer. For every inch the weir

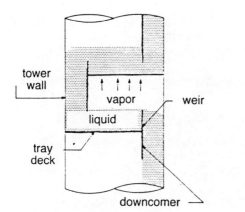

tower wall

vapor

liquid

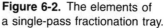

weir

tray deck

downcomer

Figure 6-2. The elements of a single-pass fractionation tray.

is lowered, tower capacity will increase 2-3%. In practice, it is not a good idea to drop weir height unless the trays are installed reasonably level.

Trays can also be expanded by replacing single-pass trays (as shown in Figure 6-3) with dual-pass trays. A dual-pass tray has two weirs per tray and has a capacity 15-25% greater than a single-pass tray. Personally, I have had some bad experiences in making this switch. The problem arose from the reduction in flow-path length (i.e., the horizontal distance between the downcomer and the weir) in converting from single- to dual-pass trays. The greater the flow-path length, the better the fractionation efficiency per tray. The tower I was revamping, an old reboiled absorber in El Dorado, Arkansas, had single-pass trays with a 36-inch flow-path length. I had these trays replaced with dual-pass trays with an 18-inch flow-path length. The predicted capacity increase was achieved; unfortunately, tower tray efficiency was so degraded that the old trays had to be reinstalled.

One safe method of expanding tray capacity is to replace the tray decks with rounded, Venturi-type holes in the tray decks. The Venturi openings reduce pressure drop per tray by about 10% and will increase tower capacity by roughly 5%. Other than cost, there is no process debit for converting to Venturi-type trays.

Other claimed methods of increasing tray capacity are:

▶ Increasing tray deck hole area.
▶ Using sweptback weirs.
▶ Sloping downcomers.
▶ Use of antijump baffles in the center downcomers of dual-pass trays.
▶ Recessed sumps under the downcomers. (This effectively increases downcomer length.)

Figure 6-3. FLEXITRAY® valve with downcomer. (Courtesy of Koch Engineering Company, Inc. Koch Engineering Company, Inc. manufactures various equipment under the FLEXITRAY®, FLEXIGRID™, and FLEXIPAC® trademarks. FLEXIPAC® elements are manufactured by Koch Engineering Company, Inc. under exclusive license of Sulzer Brothers Ltd., for the U.S.A., Canada, and Mexico.)

Packed Towers

The best results in expanding tower capacity occurs when utilizing ring-type packing in small-diameter distillation columns. In large-diameter (10 feet and over) low-pressure towers, there are definite disadvantages in using rings to pack the tower (see Chapter 2).

In one debutanizer the capacity of the tower was increased by 40% by replacing bubble-cap trays with cascade minirings. This particular tower carried gasoline overhead into the butane product whenever the feed rate rose above 18,000 BSD. By modifying the tower, as shown in Figure 6-4, 25,000 BSD of feed can be charged to the debutanizer without flooding the tower.

Operating data on this tower after it was packed showed an HETP (height equivalent of theoretical plate) of 39 inches. This is about the same as is usually obtained in debutanizers with a 24-inch spacing between trays. Hence, the 40% increase in capacity was obtained with no sacrifice in tower fractionation efficiency.

The two redistributors were the most important feature in this tower that contributed to the favorably low HETP. The purpose of these redistributors is to distribute vapor and liquid that may have become channeled as they passed through the packing. A similar debutanizer, which operated in parallel and in identical service with the tower shown in Figure 6-4, had a HETP of about six feet. The only difference between the two debutanizers was that the tower with the greater HETP did not have redistributors. Based on this experience, and in contradiction to the advice of several vendors, I never design packed towers with a continuous packing bed of more than 20 feet.

Note that the packing at the bottom of each bed for the tower illustrated in Figure 6-4 is one size larger than the bulk of the packing in that bed. This feature prevents the interface between the support grid and the packing from becoming a pinch point and causing premature tower flooding. The packing is distributed by size so that the smallest packing is utilized in those parts of the debutanizer with the lower vapor-liquid loads. The smaller the packing, the less its capacity; but the greater its fractionation efficiency. For example, in one application 2-inch metal pall rings had an HETP of 20 inches; whereas, the corresponding number for 1-inch metal pall rings was 14 inches.

Overhead Condensers

An operating distillation column that has insufficient condenser capacity will overpressure unless the excess uncondensed vapors accumulating in the reflux drum are vented off. To avoid this situation, operators adjust the reflux rate downward to unload the condensers.

To expand condenser capacity, the most straightforward way is to add additional condensers in parallel to the existing units. In practice, this option is fraught with danger. The problem arises because the condensers to be added are unlikely to be identical or piped absolutely symmetrical to the existing condensers. The unfortunate results of this type of application are often:

▶ The new condensers have a relatively high pressure drop and a large amount of heat-transfer surface. In this case the tower overhead vapors preferentially take the path of least resistance and largely pass through the old set of condensers.
RESULT: The surface area in the new set of condensers is mostly wasted.
▶ The new set of condensers have a relatively low pressure drop and a small amount of heat-transfer surface. Now, the vapors mostly flow into the new condensers.
RESULT: The surface area of the new heat exchangers is insufficient to condense all the vapors, and uncondensed vapors pass into the reflux drum. I have actually witnessed one installation where a new set of parallel overhead condensers were commissioned. Not only was no capacity increase achieved, but much to the dismay of the process designer, net overhead condensing ability was lost.

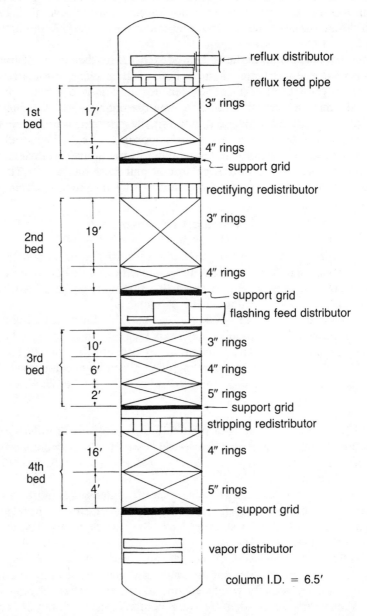

Figure 6-4. A properly designed packed tower can increase capacity by 40% over a trayed tower.

The circumstances described previously are most significant when the distillation tower overhead is to be totally condensed. For partial condensers, a little engineering effort to obtain balanced hydraulics between the new and old set of exchangers will lead to a workable design. For the total condensation case, the most cost-effective method for increasing condenser capacity is depicted in Figure 6-5. A low pressure drop partial condenser is added upstream and in series with the existing total condenser.

This scheme expands the total overhead condensing capacity without any concern as to vapor maldistribution due to uneven pressure drops. But, one may ask, will the tower overhead system pressure drop increase due to the pressure drop in the new condenser or the increased pressure drop caused by the larger overhead vapor flow?

The answer is no. The overhead system pressure drop can actually be reduced by locating a low pressure drop partial condenser ahead of existing total condensers! The new exchanger will decrease the pounds of pressure drop producing vapors that the old condenser handles. Of course, the total pounds of fluid remains constant. But it is the vapor, and not the liquid, that causes pressure drop in condensers. The new exchanger, being only a partial condenser, can easily be designed for a low pressure drop. Table 6-1 shows the results of one such modification.

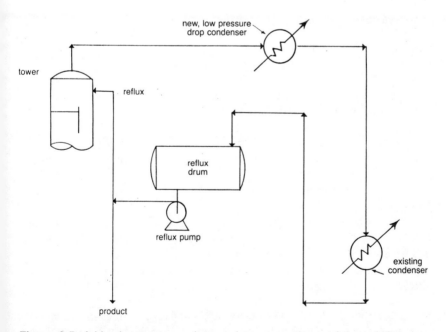

Figure 6-5. Add a low pressure drop exchanger upstream of the existing condenser to expand condensing capacity.

Table 6-1
Pressure Drops in Depropanizer Overhead System

Pressure Drop (psi)		Flow (pounds per hour)	
		25,000 Without a Partial Condenser	35,000 With a Partial Condenser
New partial condenser		None	2 psi
Old total condenser		8 psi	5 psi
	Total	8 psi	7 psi

Fin-Tube Exchangers

A widespread method of enhancing condenser surface area is to retube the tube bundle with low fin tubes. The heat-transfer surface area will be increased by approximately 2½ times. However, there are certain definite drawbacks to this option:

▶ If the controlling resistance to heat transfer is on the tube side, fin tubes have no advantage over conventional smooth tubes because

$$U = \frac{1}{R_s + R_t \times \dfrac{A_s}{A_t}}$$

where:
U = overall heat-transfer coefficient.
R_s = shell-side resistance to heat transfer.
R_t = tube-side resistance to heat transfer.
A_t = heat-transfer surface as measured on the inside of the tubes.
A_s = heat-transfer surface as measured on the outside of the tubes.

For smooth tubes, the factor A_s/A_t is about 1.2; for finned tubes, A_s/A_t is about 2.8.

Thus, if R_t is large compared to R_s, finned tubes will not gain heat-transfer capacity, as the increased surface area will be offset by the reduced U (heat-transfer coefficient). For example, a condenser with a heavy fouling deposit on the tube side will not be a good candidate for retubing with finned tubes.

▶ If the shell-side fluid is very dirty or corrosive, fin tubes may have less heat-transfer potential than smooth tubes. Particulate matter will lodge between the fins and provide a site for the growth of very heavy fouling deposits, which then reduce heat transfer. On one alkylation unit deisobutanizer I worked on, we doubled condenser capacity by discarding the finned-tube condensers in favor of plain-tube bundles.

Assuming that properly treated water is circulating through the tube side on a condenser and that the shell-side vapors are noncorrosive and free of heavy oil, replacing a smooth-tube bundle with a finned-tube bundle will increase condenser capacity by 60-90%.

Reboilers

The obvious solution to a heat input capacity limitation is to install a second reboiler in parallel with the existing unit. This is a difficult project to implement unless the new reboiler is installed absolutely symmetrical and is identical to the existing reboiler. If it is not, liquid will flow preferentially to one of the reboilers, while the other is starved for liquid and runs dry. The reboiler that runs dry will begin to foul, and this fouling will further reduce liquid flow to the reboiler.

Assuming that inlet valves have been installed ahead of each reboiler, the flows may be adjusted by partially closing the valve to the reboiler with a low outlet temperature. Not only is this an operational headache, but running a reboiler with a partially closed inlet valve may promote fouling.

Reboilers can best be operated in parallel by providing a separate draw-off nozzle for each exchanger. This type of arrangement is shown in Figure 6-6. If separate trap-out pans are used, do not forget to install a balancing line connecting both pans. A balancing line will help equalize the flow to each reboiler.

It may be possible to connect a second reboiler in series with the existing exchanger. Processwise this is OK, provided that there is sufficient hydrostatic head to drive the distillation tower bottoms through both reboilers (see Chapter 7). On new tower installations, I have often seen reboilers operating in series with no problem, but I have never seen a successful retrofit project where reboilers were piped in series.

Optimum Reboiler Retrofit

Nine times out of ten, the best way to add a new reboiler to an existing distillation tower is to utilize the low-temperature reboiler concept. Figure 6-7 illustrates this idea. A new draw-off nozzle and trap-out pan are installed about one-third up the stripping section from the bottom tray. This installation requires the removal of one or two trays. Liquid from the new nozzle is piped to a new reboiler set at grade. The reboiler vaper-liquid effluent is returned to the tower on the tray below the new draw-off nozzle.

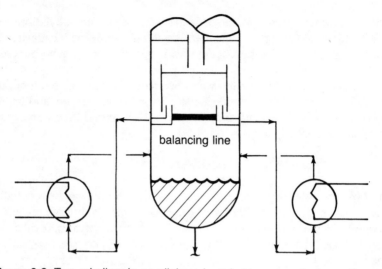

Figure 6-6. Two reboilers in parallel are best fed by separate draw-off nozzles.

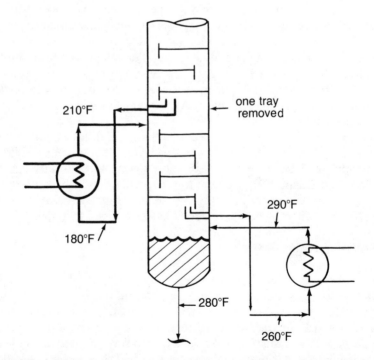

Figure 6-7. A liquid draw-off part way up the tower is the preferred method for installing a second reboiler.

The advantage of this scheme is that circulation through the existing reboiler is not impaired. Also, vapor and liquid traffic across the lower trays is reduced. As these are usually the maximum loaded trays in the tower, a substantial tower capacity gain can be achieved.

The disadvantage is that stripping efficiency of the trays between the two reboilers is somewhat reduced due to the reduction in vapor traffic in this section of the tower. This reduction can amount to a loss of one or two theoretical equilibrium separation stages.

Energy Savings

The use of a low-temperature reboiler, as shown in Figure 6-7, can be a very effective method of saving energy. In one plant a distillation column was reboiled with 100-psig steam. Nearby, waste 25 psig was being vented. The low-pressure steam was too cool to replace the 100-psig steam in the bottoms reboiler. However, by retrofitting the tower with a draw-off nozzle six trays from the bottom and a new reboiler, half the heat duty was supplied from the formerly vented 25-psig steam. The new reboiler operated 60°F below the bottoms reboiler.

High-Flux Tubing

One company markets a specially coated tube designed to enhance nucleate boiling. The surface of these tubes appear to be quite porous. It is this property that promotes the vigorous boiling that this company claims can increase the heat transfer in thermosiphon reboilers by a factor of three.[1] Retubing an existing reboiler with high-flux tubes is an ideal way of expanding reboiler capacity—if one chooses the right application.

Of course, do not expect to be able to use these porous surface tubes in a fouling service. The pores will clog with dirt and provide sites for further fouling accumulations.

My personal experiences with this technology have been confined to two applications.

Toluene reboiler. The tower was retrofitted to utilize 100-psig steam instead of 400-psig steam by retubing the reboilers with Linde High-Flux Tubes. An overall heat-transfer coefficient of 470 Btu/hr/ft²/°F was anticipated. When commissioned, a coefficient of about 150 was observed. Finally, the process engineer on the unit decided to restrict the thermosiphon circulation rate thru the reboiler. This move increased the coefficient to about 400! The high rate of liquid circulation across the tubes evidently interferred with nucleate boiling. This is the only instance I have ever observed where *decreasing* mass velocity improved heat transfer.

Pentane reboiler. An attempt was made to replace 100-psig steam in this reboiler with 30-psig steam. Luckily, we preserved the 100-psig steam connection, because the project was a failure. The Linde tubes were supposed to increase the heat-transfer coefficient from 120 to 440 Btu/hr/ft²/°F. Unfortunately, no substantial increase in the heat-transfer coefficient was observed.

Fin tubes can be used in reboiler service, as they are used to expand condensing capacity. However, as reboilers are more prone to fouling than condensers, the applications for finning reboiler tubes are limited. Changing tube metallurgy from carbon steel to a corrosion-resistant stainless steel (304 S.S., 316 S.S.) will usually increase the service heat-transfer coefficient by reducing tube surface pitting. This eliminates the sites where fouling deposits initiate their growth.

Reference

1. Union Carbide, Technical Information Bulletin, High-Flux Tubing, September 1979.

7

Distillation Tower
Reboiler Details

Jim Richard was my predecessor in the Amoco Oil Process Design Department. I sat at his desk and was issued his calculator. His last day at Amoco's Chicago office overlapped with the start of my career.

My new boss, Bill Dupray, turned over all Jim's half-finished projects to me with a word of caution, "Jim Richard was the most dedicated, thorough engineer in the department. Every design he turned out was mathematically optimized. His material balance calculations checked out to the pound."

Bill Dupray pulled at his thin, graying hair and continued, "But I need to tell you that Jim never completed any assignments. He never actually turned out any designs from which we could construct equipment. He never liked to issue final design reports."

Bill paused to scratch at a spot on his tie and went on. "The one time Jim Richard did finish a job it was for the El Dorado Depropanizer—he worked on it for six months. That was 10 years ago. It was a fine job, which used computerized modeling of a fractionation tower. Unfortunately, the tower never worked."

"What do you mean, it never worked?"

"Well," Bill responded, "we could never get the tower to separate propane and butane. The El Dorado refinery manager was so incensed about the tower that he had it torn down and sent its nameplate, along with a nasty note, to the Vice President of Engineering. After that, Jim became more interested in doing preliminary studies than final equipment designs."

"But Bill, what was so wrong with the depropanizer that it couldn't be fixed?"

"Oh, it was just a few details that Jim got wrong, but perhaps I'd better tell you about them."

Unfolding a yellowed, and not overly clean design report, Bill explained.

Kettle Reboilers

"Figure 7-1 shows a generalized sketch of a depropanizer. The reboiler shown is a standard thermosyphon type. Jim preferred kettle reboilers over thermosyphon reboilers and that led to his big mistake on the depropanizer. Figure 7-2 shows the kettle reboiler used on this job.

"Liquid from the bottom of the depropanizer tower flows by gravity into the shell side of the kettle. A baffle at the end of the shell maintains a liquid level in the kettle sufficient to submerge the topmost tube of the tube bundle. Hot oil or steam flows through the tubes and boils the liquid. The vapors thus generated flow out of the kettle, into the vapor outlet line, and up into the depropanizer. A vapor space (usually 1-2 feet) is left between the boiling liquid level and the top of the shell to disengage entrained liquid before the vapors enter the outlet line.

"The unvaporized liquid overflows the baffle into a small surge area at the end of the kettle. Liquid drawn off from this point is the depropanizer bottoms product. The liquid is drawn off at a rate sufficient to maintain a level below the baffle.

"In addition to the usual heat-transfer problems associated with sizing the exchanger surface area, there are some very delicate hydraulic questions in setting the elevations of the tower nozzles which are piped up to the kettle reboiler shell.

"What is the driving force that propels the depropanizer bottoms out of the tower, into and through the kettle reboiler tube bundle, and over the baffle? This force is the liquid head between the top of the liquid in the tower bottoms and the top of the liquid in the boiling end of the kettle. In Figure 7-2 this driving force is labeled 'liquid head driving force':

$$P_D = (H_+ - H_k) \times D_L/2.31$$

where:

P_D = liquid head driving force, psig.
H_+ = height of liquid in the bottom of the tower, feet.
H_k = height of the liquid in the boiling side of the kettle reboiler, feet.
D_L = density of the liquid in the bottom of the tower, pounds per cubic feet.

"This liquid driving force must equal the sum of the following pressure drops:

▶ Friction loss in the liquid inlet line. This is usually a small pressure drop.
▶ Entrance loss in the kettle inlet nozzle. In this particular design this proved to be a big problem, which is discussed later.

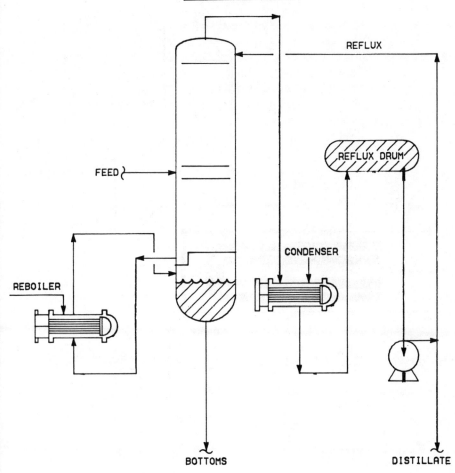

Figure 7-1. A typical refinery distillation tower.

▶ Pressure drop across the tube bundle. For a stagnant boiling liquid exchanger, this pressure loss is usually 0.5 psig or less.

▶ Friction loss of the vapors in the vapor outlet line. Unfortunately, if the vapor space above the liquid level in the kettle is too small, liquid is sucked up in this vapor line. The entrained liquid greatly increases the pressure loss in the vapor line.

"If it then transpires that the sum of these pressure drops exceed P_D, the liquid head driving force, then the height of liquid in the bottom of the

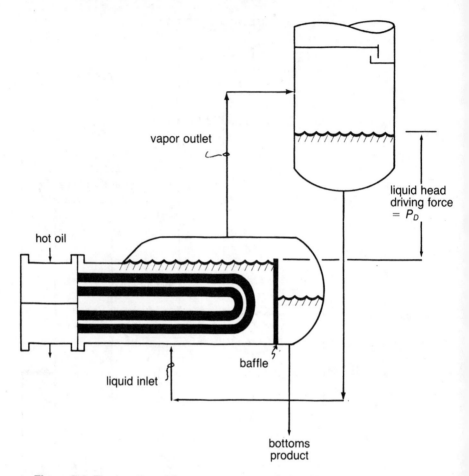

Figure 7-2. The location of the vapor return nozzle is critical in a tower served by a kettle reboiler.

depropanizer tower begins to rise until a pressure balance is reestablished. This is OK until the liquid level reaches the reboiler vapor-return nozzle. As soon as the bottoms level reaches this height, the vapor will begin to entrain massive amounts of liquid up into the bottom tray of the tower. The bottom tray will flood, which will cause flooding in the entire column. The end result will be a complete loss in fractionation efficiency. This sequence of events is exactly what happened at the El Dorado Depropanizer.

"The first mistake that Jim Richard made in his design was not allowing for the height of liquid over the top of the baffle

$$H = .0045 \left(\frac{Q}{L}\right)^{.67}$$

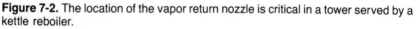

where:

H = height of liquid over the top of the baffle, feet.

Q = flow of liquid over the top of the baffle, gpm.

L = length of the baffle at the level at which the liquid overflows, feet.

For instance, if the depropanizer bottoms product is 400 gpm, and the baffle is 1 foot wide at its top, the liquid level on the left-hand side of the baffle (see Figure 7-2) will be 3 inches above the top of the baffle. This not only reduces P_D (the liquid head driving force), but more important, severely decreases the space available for vapor-liquid disengagement."

Bill paused for a moment to study the spot on his tie, "So you can see that when Jim forgot to take into account the height of the liquid as it passed over the baffle, he caused the liquid to be entrained into the vapor outlet line. This then caused a high pressure drop in the vapor outlet line, which caused the liquid level in the bottom of the tower to rise."

"That's kind of an easy point to miss in a design," I suggested.

"I suppose so," Bill answered, "but the consequences were rather terrible, considering the other mistake that Jim made. You see, the location he chose for the liquid entrance nozzle to the kettle reboiler led to a very high pressure drop. It's difficult to explain, but the tube bundle slides into the shell across two angle irons welded to the bottom of the shell. The tube support baffles rest on these angle irons. In effect, the two angle irons and the tube support baffles formed the four sides of a box. Jim located the inlet nozzle right underneath the box. This made it difficult for the inlet liquid to spread out into the reboiler bundle from the entrance nozzle. The result, again, was a high pressure drop which forced the liquid in the bottom of the depropanizer to rise."

Trying to hide my confusion, I asked, "What would be the proper way to avoid the problem of high pressure drop in the inlet liquid nozzle?"

"That's easy," Bill responded, "one should use multiple liquid inlets." Bill drew Figure 7-3 to illustrate his point and continued with his explanation.

"The cumulative effect of these errors caused the depropanizer to flood whenever an appreciable amount of heat was applied to the reboiler. The liquid level in the bottom of the tower would rise above the vapor return nozzle. As soon as the liquid reached this point, the whole tower would begin flooding. Within a half hour, liquid could be observed in the depropanizer overhead vapor line.

"Of course, none of these internal problems with the kettle reboiler would ever have been noticed if Jim had specified a reasonable height for the distance between the bottom of the depropanizer tower and the top of the kettle reboiler. To provide enough driving force to overcome the pressure drops associated with circulating liquid through the kettle, a distance of 20

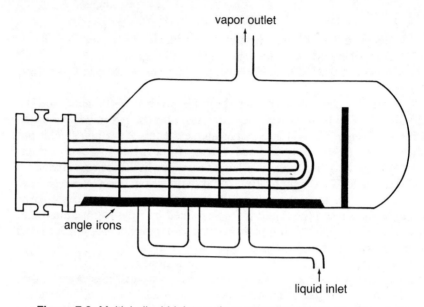

Figure 7-3. Multiple liquid inlets reduce pressure drop in a kettle reboiler.

feet should have been provided between the maximum liquid level (which is the same as the vapor return nozzle) and the top of the baffle inside the kettle. Unfortunately, Jim never was too keen about this type of detail, so he only allowed six feet to minimize the total height of the depropanizer structure."

Thermosiphon Reboilers

"Well, we received a long letter from the El Dorado Operations Manager complaining about the depropanizer. So, we sent Jim down there to investigate. He decided that the kettle reboiler design was intrinsically inferior to a thermosiphon design and should therefore be modified. To mollify the operations people at El Dorado, we made a crash effort to implement Jim's new design.

"Basically, a thermosiphon reboiler is different from a kettle reboiler because the tower's bottom product exits from the top of the reboiler, along with the vapor. The liquid in the thermosiphon reboiler effluent drops to the bottom of the tower and is then withdrawn as the tower's bottom product. By contrast, the bottoms product in a distillation tower reboiled with a kettle is withdrawn from the end of the kettle.

"Here is a sketch of a standard thermosiphon reboiler," said Bill as he unfolded Figure 7-4. "Note how the liquid feed to a thermosiphon reboiler is

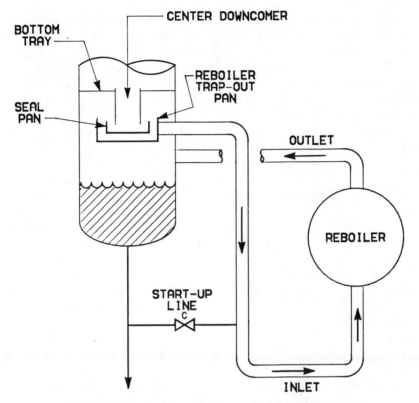

Figure 7-4. Typical thermosiphon reboiler arrangement.

withdrawn from the bottom tray of the tower; whereas in a kettle reboiler the liquid feed flows from the bottom of the tower.

"The great practical advantage of thermosiphon reboilers over kettle types is that the former are subject to less shell-side dirt accumulations. The liquid which circulates through the thermosiphon reboiler tube bundle tends to wash particulates into the bottom of the tower.

"A thermosiphon reboiler operates on the principle that the density of fluid in the inlet line (i.e., all liquid) is greater than the density of fluid in the outlet line (i.e., vapor-liquid mixture). This density difference provides the hydraulic driving force that establishes circulation through the shell. This driving force must be sufficient to prevent liquid from overflowing the trap-out pan shown in Figure 7-4.

"But, once again, Jim hadn't properly concerned himself with the details. First of all, note the start-up line shown in Figure 7-4. Without this line, liquid from the bottom tray will not flow into the reboiler on start-up. As there is no upflowing vapor on start-up, liquid leaks through the deck of the bottom tray and hence never collects in the reboiler trap-out pan. Since there is no liquid in the reboiler to generate vapors, there is no way to get the column started.

"The start-up line permits liquid from the bottom of the column to gravitate into the reboiler. Once the reboiler begins producing vapors, the start-up line is closed. Jim never worried about how equipment was started, so he omitted this detail."

I couldn't help but notice that a trace of bitterness was creeping into Bill's voice.

"Even after this omission was corrected in the field, we found that the reboiler still would not function properly. Take a close look at Figure 7-4. See how the reboiler trap-out pan is slightly higher than the seal pan? We normally make the sides of the reboiler trap-out pan 4-8 inches higher than the sides of the seal pan. This keeps the liquid overflowing the seal pan from by-passing the trap-out pan. Of course, any liquid that misses the trap-out pan will not flow into the reboiler.

"Well, Jim made the trap-out pan sides level with the seal pan sides, resulting in a reboiler starved for liquid. After the trap-out pan sides were extended up by six inches, liquid circulation through the reboiler was finally established. But then a new problem cropped up.

"Jim was careful not to repeat his earlier error of introducing a high pressure drop in the reboiler circulation loop, so he greatly oversized the reboiler outlet line. However, in a thermosiphon reboiler the outlet line carries 30-50 weight percent liquid. If this liquid is not entrained by the vapor, slug flow takes place in the vertical portion of the reboiler outlet line. To avoid slug flow, the velocity in the reboiler outlet line should be not less than 15 fps. At this velocity, the rapidly flowing vapor will evenly entrain the liquid leaving the top of the reboiler. When we went back and checked Jim's calculations, we found that he had designed the reboiler outlet line for 3 fps.

"The slug flow from the reboiler caused a constant fluctuation in both the depropanizer tower's bottom liquid level and top pressure."

"I suppose that the oversized reboiler outlet line was also rectified?"

Bill studied his soiled tie for several minutes before answering, "No, that was the last straw. The El Dorado refinery manager claimed that the Chicago Engineering Office was staffed by incompetent fools. He had the depropanizer torn down and sent its nameplate to Dr. White, our Vice President. Jim took the incident rather personally. He has a fine mind, but never could get enthused with details.

"I saw Jim Richard just last week. He's teaching philosophy at Northwestern University. Surrounded by a group of admiring students, he seemed to be quite at home."

8

Sizing Vessels

Of all the various types of process equipment, drum design is the simplest. Yet even in the specification of drums, there is ample room for error. For instance, in one refinery that I helped commission, the designer had omitted the "riser" in every reflux drum. The purpose of the riser, as shown in Figure 8-1, is to reduce water entrainment in the hydrocarbon liquid outlet.

The riser is the same diameter as the outlet nozzle and is typically six inches high. A vortex breaker in the form of two crossed vertical plates should be set on top of the riser. The cross should be two or three inches high.

For the riser to function properly, the water layer in the bottom of the reflux drum must be less than the height of the riser—six inches. A water draw-off boot is set below the reflux drum. The water which settles out of the hydrocarbon liquid runs across the bottom of the drum and into the draw-off boot.

Most draw-off boots are an integral part of the reflux drum. Practical experience has shown this type of design to be a mistake. The reflux drum is almost always elevated 15-25 feet above grade to provide net positive suction head (NPSH) for the reflux pump. This puts the water draw-off boot at a 10-20-foot elevation—well out of easy reach of operating personnel. It is a fact of refinery life that most operators will not bother to climb a 15-foot ladder to routinely check a water level in a boot.

Locating the water draw-off boot at grade is a little more expensive than attaching it to the reflux drum, but it will certainly improve operator attention to maintaining the critical water-hydrocarbon interface level. For those applications where the water in the reflux drum is to be drained manually rather than automatically through a control valve, locating the water draw-off boot at grade should be mandatory.

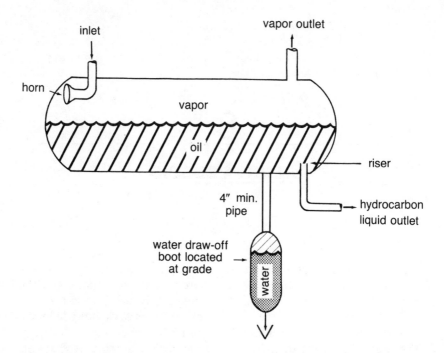

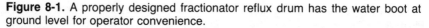

Figure 8-1. A properly designed fractionator reflux drum has the water boot at ground level for operator convenience.

Do not make the line connecting the bottom of the drum to the top of the boot too small. Water draw-offs are inherently subject to plugging. A four-inch line is a practical minimum.

Sizing the Boot

If the boot is drained on level control through a control valve, a water residence time of 7½ minutes half full is sufficient. Size the dimensions of the boot so that the normal interface level is 4-5 feet above grade (i.e., at eye level).

If the boot is to be drained manually, it must be sized to hold the volume of water anticipated to accumulate in not less than four hours. It is not good design practice to expect an operator to drain a vessel more frequently than twice a shift.

A high interface level alarm is required, regardless of whether level control is manual or automatic. Do not forget that the consequences of refluxing water into a hydrocarbon distillation tower can be extremely adverse—greatly accelerated rates of corrosion and an immediate loss in fractionation efficiency will result.

Hydrocarbon-Water Separation

The rate of settling of water droplets in a hydrocarbon continuous phase can be calculated from Stokes' law

$$S = \frac{2\ gr^2\ (P_L - P_w)}{9V}$$

where:
  S = rate (velocity) of a droplet settling under the influence of gravity.
  g = gravitational constant.
  V = viscosity of the continuous phase—in this case liquid hydrocarbon.
  r = radius of the droplet.
  $P_L - P_w$ = The density differences between the two phases.

In practice, Stokes' law is usually of little value because the particle size distribution is rarely known to the designer. A general rule of thumb for determining the rate of settling of condensed water in hydrocarbons varying in density and viscosity from butane through diesel oil is:

▶ 20 feet per hour or less (settling of water substantially complete).
▶ 30-50 feet per hour (reasonably good settling).
▶ 90 feet per hour or more (incomplete settling expected).

Figure 8-2 illustrates the vertical settling distance in a horizontal reflux drum. The water level shown can be considered as the height of the riser shown in Figure 8-1. The hydrocarbon liquid level is the normal liquid level.

From the previous considerations, it might appear that the settling of water is enhanced by sizing reflux drums with a large length-to-diameter ratio. This is probably true. However, in practice, horizontal drums are designed with a 3 or 4 length-to-diameter ratio.

Inlet Piping Design

The principal reason reflux drums—even those that do not separate vapor from liquid—are not sized long and thin is to reduce the horizontal component of liquid velocity. This reduction minimizes turbulence and thus promotes the settling of water into the draw-off boot.

The design of the inlet nozzle can also influence turbulence in a drum. Obviously, if the feed to a vessel is permitted to fall directly down, the liquid in the drum will be agitated. To avoid agitation, the inlet stream is turned 90°

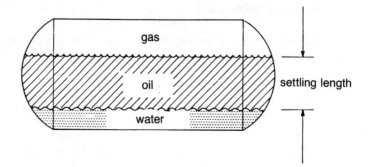

Figure 8-2. Droplets of water will usually settle through the oil layer at a rate of 25-30 feet per hour.

with an internal elbow to splash against the head of the drum. Also, as shown in Figure 8-1, the end of the internal elbow is flared-out. This feature also tends to reduce agitation of liquid in the drum.

The distance between the inlet nozzle and the three outlet (water, hydrocarbon, vapor) nozzles should be at a maximum. The water drain nozzle and the riser (i.e., the hydrocarbon outlet) can be next to each other.

A Word of Caution

Some mixtures of water and organic liquids settle very, very slowly. Certainly, 10° API (1.0 sp gr) aromatic oil will never separate from water by gravity. Liquids with viscosities much greater than 20-50 centipoise settle out much slower than the foregoing rules of thumb indicate. Certain organics, such as sodium napthenates, form very tight emulsions with water. Surfactants, which reduce the surface tension of water, also impede the separation of oil and water.

If a water-oil mixture is formed by throttling the fluid through a control valve, the tightness of the emulsion will be proportional to the pressure drop taken across the valve. Passing water and oil together through a centrifugal pump will greatly increase the settling time required to separate the two phases.

Rather than guess at a settling rate for unusual services, the designer should perform settling rate experiments in the laboratory. This approach is easier than replacing an undersized reflux drum in the field.

Flooded Condenser Reflux Drum

The flooded condenser is the most common form of pressure control in distillation towers with total overhead condensation. In this application the reflux drum normally is 100% full of liquid. The system works on the principle of backing up liquid out of the reflux drum into the overhead condensers to raise tower pressure.

Important points to remember in designing reflux drums for this service are:

▶ *Withdraw the net product from the reflux pump discharge.* Do not expect to pressure the liquid out of the drum. The liquid can be at its bubble point and hence will start to vaporize in the product rundown line.

▶ *The reflux drum is only nominally liquid full.* When it becomes unflooded due to limited condensing capacity, a vapor vent will be required. A low liquid level alarm is of vital importance. This device will alert the operators that the reflux drum is filling with vapor and must be vented to protect the reflux pumps.

Liquid Hold Time

A certain amount of surge volume is required in every reflux drum. The conventional rule is to calculate this volume to provide 7½ minutes hold time to the high liquid level. In practice, it is wise to consider the requirements for each service individually.

For instance, consider the vessel shown in Figure 8-3. There are three distinct portions in this drum:

▶ *The volume between the normal and high liquid level alarms.* This is the maximum operating range. Its volume should ordinarily be based on net product. If the product is to be rundown to a tank, a five-minute surge time is sufficient. On the other hand, if the reflux drum net effluent is used to charge another distillation tower, a steadier flow will be necessary. In this case, a 10-12 minute hold time is reasonable. If the reflux ratio is high, a hold time of not less than two minutes between the high liquid and low liquid level alarms based on gross (reflux plus product) overhead is correct.

▶ *The volume below the low liquid level alarm.* When the oil level falls to within several inches of the top of the riser, the reflux pump will lose suction and begin cavitating. The designer may assume the operating personnel will take corrective action once the low liquid level alarm sounds. If the distillation tower is adjacent to a fully staffed control center, two minutes hold time based on net product is sufficient for the volume between the low liquid level alarm and the top of the riser. For a service located in a remote, unmanned area, the designer should approximate the required surge volume based on how long it will take a person to reach the reflux pump.

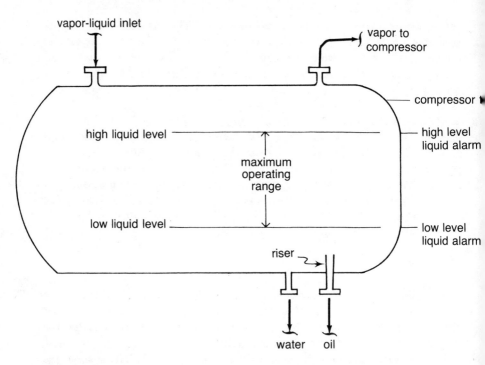

Figure 8-3. The consequence of a low or high level must be considered when sizing a reflux drum.

▶ *The volume above the high liquid level alarm.* When the oil level rises to a critical height based on the velocity of the vapor, massive entrainment of liquid into the vapor outlet nozzle will result. If the vapors then pass through a downstream separator, the carryover of liquid may not be too critical. However, if, as illustrated in Figure 8-3, a compressor is taking suction directly from the drum, extreme caution is in order. A slug of liquid entering a high-speed centrifugal compressor will severely damage the compressor's rotor. Good design practice is to provide an automatic shutdown device to trip off the compressor when the liquid rises to the critical entrainment level. The hold time between the high liquid level alarm and the compressor trip level should be not less than three minutes. Again, depending on the distance between the vessel and the nearest operator, and the consequences to the process of shutting down the compressor, the designer may choose to increase this time substantially.

There is no sense basing hold-time calculations on the assumption that operating personnel will not promptly respond to level alarms. If an alarm is going to be ignored, it can just as easily be ignored for 10 minutes as for 2 minutes.

The vessel volume shown in Figure 8-3 above the compressor trip level is devoted to vapor-liquid separation. The required volume for this purpose is a function of vapor velocity, vapor-liquid density difference, and permissible entrainment.

Vapor-Liquid Separators

A vertical knockout drum, as shown in Figure 8-4, is most often used to settle entrained liquid droplets from a flowing gas stream. The objective is to reduce the velocity of the gas enough to permit the larger droplets of liquid

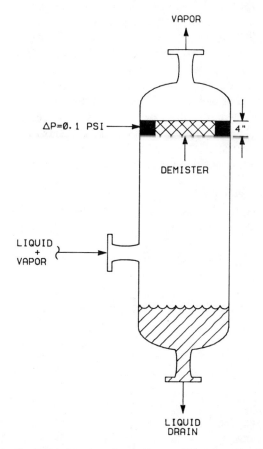

Figure 8-4. A simple vertical knock-out drum will have a greater capacity with a demister.

to drop into the bottom of the drum. To calculate the maximum vertical velocity, the following formula is used:

$$S = K \left(\frac{P_L - P_V}{P_V} \right)^{\frac{1}{2}}$$

where:
S = maximum vertical velocity, fps.
P_L = density of liquid.
P_V = density of vapor.
K = a constant defined in Table 8-1.

Figure 8-4 shows a demister pad placed in front of the vapor outlet. This is a rather common device. The droplets of liquid impinge and are coalesced on the Brillolike fibers of the demister pad. Pressure drop across a clean demister is negligible—except for vacuum service. For example, air blown through a 4-inch demister at 10 fps will exhibit a pressure drop of only 1-inch of water. Do not use demisters in fouling services, as they will cake up with debris. Certain processes (sulfuric acid and elemental sulfur are two) produce fine mists that can only be coalesced and settled with demisters. Field tests have shown that demisters in these services do not function properly at low velocities. This is because the droplets of fine liquid must impinge on the demister fibers with a certain momentum to coalesce properly. The guidelines in Table 8-1 should be followed to avoid this difficulty.

The vertical distance between the top of the inlet nozzle and the tangent line of the top head (or the bottom of the demister) should be at least one vessel diameter. When setting the distance between the bottom of the inlet

Table 8-1
Constants for Sizing Vertical Vapor-Liquid Separates

	K Factor	
	Without Demister	With Demister
Minimum entrainment	0.15	0.30
Moderate-pressure service minimum entrainment	0.10	0.20
High (1000 + psi) H_2 service moderate entrainment	0.25	0.45
Severe entrainment	0.50	—
De-entrainment of steam	—	0.20

nozzle and the maximum liquid level, remember that once the liquid level rises to the height of the inlet nozzle, massive entrainment will follow.

Horizontal Vapor-Liquid Separators

When a large volume of liquid is involved, a horizontal vapor-liquid separator is more cost effective than a vertical knockout drum. The volume of the drum devoted to vapor-liquid separation is above the maximum permissible liquid level (i.e., above the compressor trip in Figure 8-3). The maximum horizontal component of velocity is calculated using the same formula as for vertical drums, with the exception that the K factor (no demister) is 0.034 for minimum entrainment of liquid.

Hydrocarbon Skimming Vessel

The converse of an ordinary reflux drum equipped to drain off small quantities of water, is the hydrocarbon skimming vessel shown in Figure 8-5. A feed drum in rich amine service is a common example.

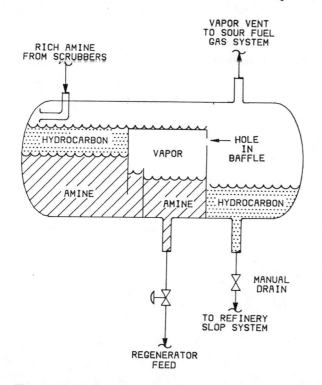

Figure 8-5. Hydrocarbon skimming vessel (drawn to scale).

The baffle heights shown in the sketch are drawn to scale based on separating an aqueous phase (1.0 sp gr) from a lighter-oil phase (0.7-0.9 sp gr). The left-hand section of the vessel is used for separating the hydrocarbons from the aqueous phase. It should have a residence time of about seven minutes. The middle and right-hand compartments are used for surge volume and should be sized accordingly.

I have used this design in several applications with very good results. Its principal advantage over a conventional, manually operated skimming drum is the minimum operator attention required.

9

Steam Surface Condensers
for Turbines

The industrial revolution was kicked off with the introduction of steam-driven pumps to evacuate the flooded coal mines of England. Both the pumps and the drivers were huge reciprocating machines. After passing through the engine, the exhaust steam was vented to the atmosphere. Later on, it was discovered that a great deal more work could be extracted from steam if it was exhausted to a chamber maintained at subatmospheric pressure. The steam's heat of condensation was removed with a cold water spray. Condensed steam was drained out of the chamber by gravity through a "barometric leg." This meant the chamber had to be elevated 20-30 feet above grade. The condensation chamber came to be called a barometric condenser.

To permit the steam condensate to be recovered and recycled back to the boiler, the surface condenser was introduced. The surface condenser is a shell-and-tube heat exchanger with special adaptations for condensing large volumes of steam under a vacuum. The term "surface" refers to the steam condensed on a cool metal surface, rather than in direct contact with cold water.

In a modern process plant 90% of the drivers will be electric motors. Of the remaining 10%, most will be small-horsepower (30-300) turbines driven by steam exhausting to a low-pressure steam header or to atmosphere. These turbines are there to provide a backup to the electric-driven machines in case of a power failure. For example, the spare for a boiler feed water motor-driven pump should be driven by a steam turbine. In case of an electric power interruption the boiler can still continue to operate.

The few steam turbines that exhaust to a surface condenser are often used to drive the largest pumps and compressors in the plant. The reasons for this are:

▶ *Economy of scale.* The complex auxiliaries that are required to operate the surface condenser are too expensive to install when only small quantities of steam are involved.

▶ *Energy saving due to variable speed.* The most energy-efficient way to control a pump or compressor is by varying the speed of the driver. Common electric motors are fixed-speed machines, where the speed of steam turbines may be easily varied. However, if a substantial amount of the potential work in the steam is not to be wasted, a "steam rack" must be used to control the turbines' speed. Steam racks are only supplied with large steam turbines.

▶ *Dependability.* Loss of a process plant's largest driver will usually shut the plant down. The plant's steam supply, originating from a multitude of sources (fired boilers, process heater convective sections, waste-heat boilers) is often more dependable than the electric power supply.

A large steam turbine is in the class of 2000 horsepower; a small turbine is less than 500 horsepower. As one can see from the following description of surface condenser auxiliary design, it does not pay to bother with surface condensers for small steam turbines.

Figure 9-1 shows a typical arrangement for a centrifugal turbine and surface condenser. Note that the condenser does not need to be below the turbine. If the exhaust steam line is large enough, the condenser can be located at a considerable distance from the turbine. The pressure drop in the turbine exhaust line will reduce the turbine's efficiency.

There are three principal components to be considered in designing a surface condenser system:

▶ The shell-and-tube exchanger.
▶ The vacuum-jet system used to pull off noncondensible gases from the shell.
▶ The condensate pumpout system.

Figure 9-2 illustrates the importance of condenser vacuum on turbine efficiency. For 150-psia steam superheated to 400°F, the work extracted from 1 pound of steam will be doubled when exhausting the steam to a near-perfect vacuum (29 inches of Hg) compared to exhausting it to the atmosphere.

Figure 9-3 shows the effect of the surface condenser temperature on vacuum. Two questions which bear on the design of the component systems of the surface condenser are suggested by Figure 9-3:

▶ What temperature are we referring to when we speak of the "temperature of water inside surface condenser?"

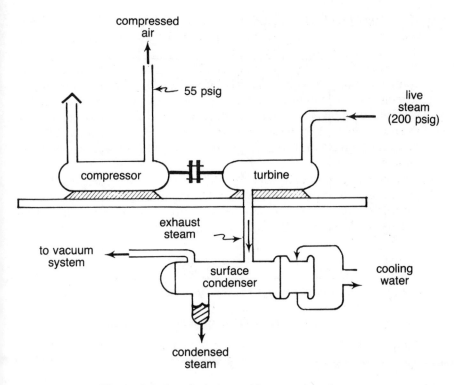

Figure 9-1. A typical steam-driven compressor.

▶ What are the factors that prevent achieving the "maximum obtainable vacuum?"

The Vacuum-Jet System

A properly designed and generously sized ejector system is the key element in a successfully designed surface condenser. The three sources of vapors to be considered in sizing the ejector-jet system are:

▶ *Air leakage.* Figure 9-4 shows a correlation to estimate air in-leakage for ejector sizing. In practice, the amount of air in-leakage for a prospective condenser is quite problematical. It is not really a function of the turbine size—the number of joints, fittings, and flanges are far more critical in accounting for air in-leakage. For a good, tightly assembled system, most of the air will be sucked in through the seal around the shaft of the turbine. A steam purge should be connected to this seal to minimize air leakage around the shaft. This is an important item for the process engineer to emphasize to the project engineer.

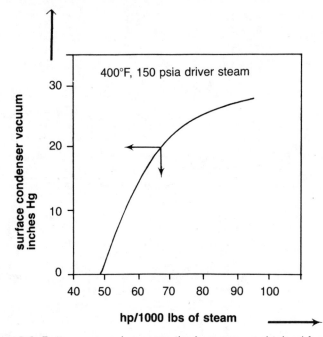

Figure 9-2. Better vaccum increases the horsepower obtained from steam.

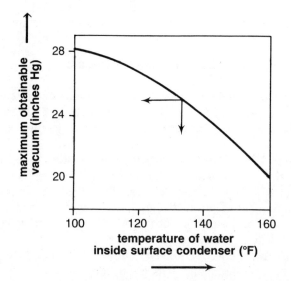

Figure 9-3. Theoretical vacuum possible in a surface condenser.

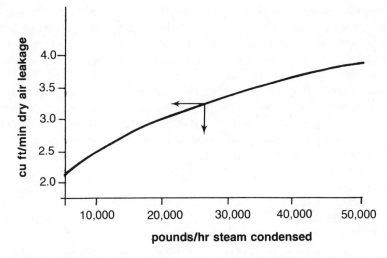

Figure 9-4. Estimated air leakage for surface condensers serving steam turbines. (Adapted from *Modern Marine Engineers Manual.*)

▶ *Carbon dioxide.* Depending on the efficiency of boiler feed water treatment, there will be a small amount of carbon dioxide in the steam supply. Considering that the air in-leakage rate used for design is just a guess and that the relative amount of CO_2 to air in ejector off-gas is small, the CO_2 contribution to ejector loading can be safely ignored.

▶ *Water vapor.* The partial pressure of water, while small, will contribute a considerable percentage of the vapor load to the first-stage jet. To calculate the quantity of water vapor, the surface condenser vapor outlet temperature and the moles of noncondensibles (in this case air) must be assumed:

$$M_{H2O} = \left(\frac{P_{H2O}}{P_t}\right) \times (M_{H2O} + M_{NC})$$

where:
M_{H2O} = moles of water vapor.
M_{NC} = moles of air.
  P_t = absolute pressure at the inlet to the first-stage ejector.
P_{H2O} = vapor pressure of water at the surface condenser outlet temperature.
then:
  $M_t = M_{H2O} + M_{NC}$
where:
  M_t = The first-stage ejector load in moles.

The previous equations are most easily solved by trial and error. Referring to Figure 9-3, it can then be seen that when the vapor pressure of water equals the total pressure, the moles of vapor to the first-stage jet become infinitely large. It is this factor which determines the maximum obtainable vacuum in a surface condenser.

Before continuing on to the design of vacuum-jet systems, note that the vapor outlet temperature in a properly designed surface condenser will be substantially higher than the condensate drain temperature. It is up to the process design engineer to specify both these temperatures when filling out the surface condenser exchanger data sheet. This involves considerations of the design of both the condensate pumpout system and the vacuum-jet system.

It is not a particularly good idea to connect several small steam turbines to a common surface condenser. On one unit five turbines all exhausted to a very large surface condenser. The jet-ejector system could barely develop any vacuum and was obviously overloaded. Unfortunately, the extreme complexity of the system made it almost impossible to identify the source of air in-leakage.

The designer may wish to double the loads listed in Figure 9-4. This will not hurt the performance of the ejectors at reduced rates. A few hundred pounds per hour of ejector steam will be wasted. The incremental installed cost of the ejectors will be small.

The vacuum-jet system should be purchased as a package from a reputable and experienced vendor. The subject of vacuum-jet design is exceedingly complex and is discussed in detail in the following chapter. Before designing the jet system, the vendor will need the following data:

▶ Moles of noncondensibles.
▶ Moles of steam.
▶ Molecular weight of noncondensibles.
▶ Steam supply temperature and pressure.
▶ Cooling-water supply and return pressure.
▶ Cooling-water supply temperature and desired return temperature (it is best to leave this last specification open to the vendor's best judgment).
▶ Required first-stage ejector inlet pressure. The final discharge pressure will be atmospheric.

Figure 9-5 shows a typical two-stage jet system. The interstage and final condensers will come as a complete package from a single vendor. The one important design feature not shown in Figure 9-5 is the drain leg from the first-stage condenser. Figure 9-6 details this often overlooked feature. Note that a loop seal is required to drain condensate back to the surface condenser from the first-stage condenser. The height of this loop seal is based on the

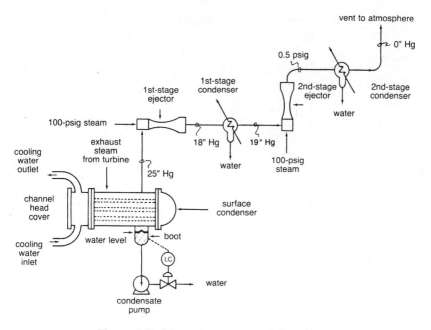

Figure 9-5. A two-stage vacuum jet system.

pressure difference between the first-stage condenser and the surface condenser

$$H_{LS} = -1.2 \, (P_{IC} - P_{SC})$$

where:
P_{IC} = pressure in the first-stage condenser, inches of Hg.
P_{SC} = pressure in the surface condenser, inches of Hg.
H_{LS} = height of liquid seal, feet.

The height of the loop seal will set the physical elevation of the vacuum-jet system. Hence, the process designer must obtain the first-stage jet discharge pressure, set the liquid seal height, and transmit this dimension to the mechanical designer.

Trying to operate a surface condenser without a loop seal allows the first-stage ejector to discharge vapors directly back to the surface condenser, and thus destroys the effectiveness of the first-stage ejector.

The process designer should insist that the ejector internals be constructed from stainless steel. An assured source of dry steam will prevent erosion of ejector internals. However, in practice, the steam to vacuum jets is often wet, and stainless steel internals are needed to prevent erosion.

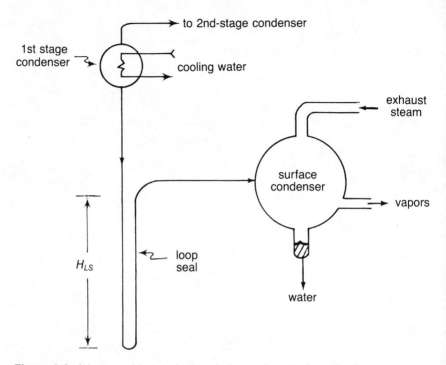

Figure 9-6. A loop seal is required to drain condensate from the first-stage condenser back to the surface condenser.

Condensate Pumpout System

The condensate pumps should be sized not for the anticipated turbine steam rate, but for the maximum amount of steam that can pass through the turbines' inlet nozzles with the steam rack wide open. If the condensate pumps cannot handle the volume of condensed steam, then water will backup into the surface condenser and slow the turbine down. On one unit, when this happened, the turbine braked down to its critical speed and self-destructed.

Include the steam used in the first-stage jet in sizing the condensate pumps. If the main turbine is supposed to operate during an electric power failure, then the spare condensate pump must itself be driven by a small steam turbine.

The major problems in operating condensate pumps servicing surface condensers are:

▶ *Seal leaks.* Unless the surface condenser is more than 30 feet above grade, the suction of the pump will be under vacuum. A slightly defective seal will then allow air to be sucked into the pump case around the shaft. A ¼ of an inch water line connected to the pump seal will eliminate this potential problem.

▶ *Marginal (NPSH).* To prevent cavitation in a centrifugal pump, the liquid flowing into the pump's suction must be below its bubble point. This is called "positive suction head." A pump in vacuum service is especially vulnerable to cavitation. Raising the surface condenser five feet higher than the minimum calculated head requirement will reduce pump cavitation problems.

▶ *Surface condenser boot size.* As shown in Figure 9-5, the condensate pump takes suction from a water leg or boot. The boot is bolted to the underside of the surface-condenser shell. The boot is sized like any other process vessel to provide:

1. A liquid hold-up time of not less than five minutes, based on the tangent-to-tangent volume.
2. A high liquid level alarm located at one-third of the boot's length below the top tangent.
3. The tangent-to-tangent boot length to be not less than three feet.
4. A vortex breaker in the bottom nozzle.

A properly designed surface condenser condensate boot is shown in Figure 9-2. If the boot is too small, the water level may rise and cover the surface condenser tubes. This will raise the exhaust steam backpressure and slow the turbine. Alternately, if the water level becomes too low, the condensate pump will lose suction and start cavitating. To restore pumping, the pump will have to be manually shutdown and restarted.

As in all pumps in vacuum service, the pump must be located directly under the boot for minimum loss of suction head due to pressure drop in the piping.

Surface Condenser

The three objectives in purchasing a surface condenser are:

▶ Adequate heat-transfer surface
▶ Adequate condensate subcooling
▶ Low pressure drop

The pressure drop in the surface condenser must be added to the exhaust steam pressure. This reduces the work that can be extracted from the driver steam and hence impairs turbine efficiency. A reasonable pressure drop in a surface condenser is 5 mm Hg (0.2 psia).

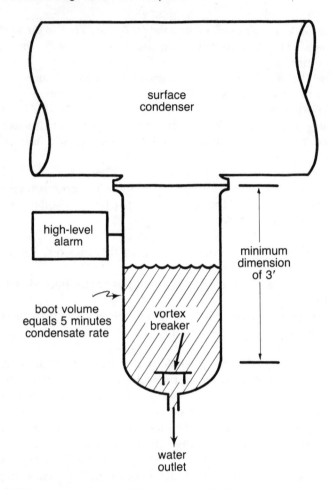

Figure 9-7. An adequately sized boot is essential for proper surface condenser operation.

The heat-transfer coefficients that can be obtained in condensing steam with clean cooling water are very high—several hundred Btu/hr/ft²/°F. To maintain this high heat-transfer coefficient in service, the tube-side water velocity should be not less than six fps. The cooling-water outlet temperature should be not more than 125°F. The exchanger should be equipped for onstream backflushing of the tubes.

One effective method for maintaining clean tubes is to brush clean the inside of each tube several times a day. There are commercially available units that will fit into an existing exchanger to accomplish cleaning. One company[1] markets a device that periodically reverses the flow of water through the tubes and moves a little brush back and forth through every tube with each flow reversal.

Using finned tubes in a surface condenser is not recommended. The controlling resistance to heat transfer will be on the tube side and in such cases finned tubes are not effective in improving heat transfer. An approach temperature of 15-20°F between the cooling-water outlet and the vapor outlet is typical. The smaller the approach temperature, the larger the surface condenser, and the greater the amount of work that can be extracted from a pound of steam.

Figure 9-8 shows a cross section of a surface condenser. Note that this exchanger has two peculiar features: a separate vapor and liquid outlet, and internal baffles used to create a collection zone where the condensate is subcooled. The condensed steam flows into a sump where it is cooled by a further 10-15°F. The tubes which pass through the subcooling zone receive the coldest water.Therefore, the water draining down into the condensate boot may actually be colder than the cooling-water outlet. The purpose of the subcooling zone is to reduce the vapor pressure of the condensate and thus increase the NPSH available for the condensate pumps.

The separate vapor outlet is required to avoid condensing the entire exhaust steam stream at a 10-15°F lower temperature. Remember that the subcooling duty is only about 10 Btu per pound, while the condensing duty is 1000 Btu per pound. The subcooling section may increase the size of the surface condenser by 10%, whereas attempting to reduce the vapor outlet temperature by 10-15°F can double the required heat-transfer surface area.

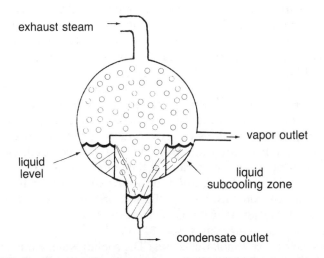

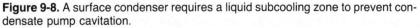

Figure 9-8. A surface condenser requires a liquid subcooling zone to prevent condensate pump cavitation.

An Unusual Incident

To conclude this chapter, I will recall a field assignment that I was given to supervise, the commissioning of a large steam turbine and air compressor. The machines had originally been built for the military in World War II as a wind tunnel to test the aerodynamics of fighter planes.

Live steam at 200-psig pressure was used to power the turbine. The steam was condensed under a vacuum. Heat from the condenser was removed with circulating cooling water. The turbine was designed to run at 4300 rpm (revolutions per minute) and compress 25,000 scfm (standard cubic feet per minute) of air from 0 to 55 psig.

To start with, the little two-stage steam ejector system would not pull a vacuum on the surface condenser (see Figure 9-5). We concluded that the condenser drain lines were plugged. I diagnosed this by observing that water blew out of the vent from the second-stage condenser. Ordinarily, just a wisp of steam should come from this vent.

After unscrewing the condenser drain legs and rodding out the pluggage, the turbine was readied for service. The steam line and turbine case were warmed up with a small amount of steam and the turbine was put on "slow roll" for 15 minutes. The steam pressure, measured at the inlet of the governor control valve, was 200 psig. As the control valve was opened, and the machine spun faster, the steam pressure slipped down. Finally, with the control valve wide open, the steam pressure bottomed-out at 120 psig with the turbine reaching only 3300 rpm, as compared to the design speed of 4300 rpm.

The steam supply pressure had been maintained at 200 psig. Engineering calculations proved that the pressure drop in the steam line should be negligible. Therefore, I had the steam supply line disassembled. Lodged firmly in one elbow were four welding rods, a broken valve handle, the top of a lunch bucket, and a withered safety shoe.

After removing this assorted junk, we started the turbine again. The steam pressure held firm at 200 psig, but the turbine speed only came up to 3500 rpm. Moreover, the vacuum in the surface condenser, which initially was 20 inches, fell off to 0 as the governor control valve was opened.

The best vacuum theoretically possible in a surface condenser corresponds to the vapor pressure of water at the temperature of the condensed steam. Figure 9-3 shows this relationship. If the condensation temperature inside the surface condenser is 212°F, the pressure inside the surface condenser cannot be less than 0 psig. The pressure of our surface condenser was 0 psig, and the temperature was 210°F.

Why was the surface condenser so hot? The cooling water exiting from the surface condenser was 175°F. This was an indication that the flow of water through the condenser's tubes was restricted. We pulled off the channel head cover (see Figure 9-5) of the condenser to see what was causing the restriction. Inside the channel head were a rubberized raincoat and several dozen paper cups.

After removing these objects, which had become lodged in the condenser's tube inlets, we reassembled the channel head. The cooling-water valves were opened and the steam inlet valves also were slowly opened. The turbine came up to its design speed of 4300 rpm—but only for a moment. Unexpectedly, the vacuum in the surface condenser, which had been holding steady at 20 inches, fell to 0.

We tried to bring the turbine up to speed again, this time taking care to observe the condensate level in the surface condenser's boot. As the steam inlet valve was opened, the level control valve on the discharge side of the condensate pump opened. When this level control valve was wide open, the water level in the boot continued to rise. After a while, the water filled the boot and began to cover the tubes inside the surface condenser. This prevented the steam from condensing and consequently raised the pressure in the surface condenser to zero psig.

We then disassembled the condensate pump, and found that the pump's impeller (the rotating part in a centrifugal pump that actually pumps the fluid) was worn down to a nub. We replaced the impeller and restarted the turbine.

This time the vacuum held, the steam supply pressure did not falter, a good level was maintained in the surface condenser's boot, and the turbine came up to 4300 rpm.

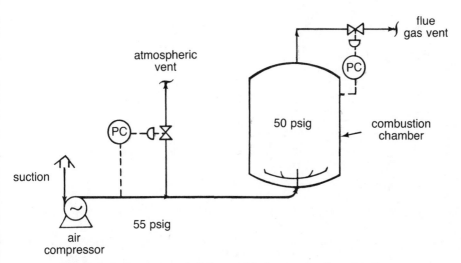

Figure 9-9. Compressed air is used in the combustion chamber.

The compressed air was vented to the atmosphere (as shown in Figure 9-9) at 55 psig. This pressure was held by a backpressure control valve in the vent line. The pressurized air was destined for use in a high-pressure combustion chamber. This combustion chamber *normally* operated at 50 psig. Hence, the compressed air could flow into the combustion chamber with no problem. This is not the end of the story.

Every piece of rotating equipment has a characteristic called "critical speed." The critical speed is related to harmonic frequency or sympathetic vibration. A turbine allowed to run at its critical speed will begin vibrating and eventually will self-destruct.

The first night that the compressed air was lined up to discharge into the combustion chamber, an operator inadvertently caused the combustion-chamber pressure to rise to 65 psig. As the steam inlet governor control valve was already wide open, the turbine slowed as the compressor's discharge pressure increased from 55 psig to 65 psig.

The turbine slowed to 3900 rpm. The critical speed of the turbine was—by coincidence—also 3900 rpm. By the time the operating crew noticed the problem, the turbine was vibrating wildly. Both the bearings and seals were later found to be severely damaged.

Reference

1. Amertap Corp. Technical Bulletin, 101 Crossway Park West, Woodbury, NY.

10

How to Pull a Deep Vacuum

Drawing a deep vacuum in a vacuum distillation column is a particularly effective method of improving product yields and reducing energy consumption.

Vacuum distillation is used to vaporize high-boiling organic liquids at temperatures low enough to prevent thermal degradation of the products. For example, petroleum tars will thermally crack (i.e., turn to gas and coke) at temperatures above 750°F. The deeper the vacuum, the lower the temperature at which the gas oils, commingled with the tar, will vaporize.

The vacuum system takes the subatmospheric process gas and compresses it to above atmospheric pressure. This stream, which is called "tail gas," consists of three components:

▶ Air which has been sucked into the vacuum distillation process through leaks.

Table 10-1
Methods of Expressing Vacuum

Very Deep Vacuum Usually expressed in mm Hg. There are 760 mm Hg at atmospheric pressure. Zero mm Hg is absolute zero pressure.
Moderate Vacuum Expressed in inches of Hg. There are 29.9 inches of Hg at absolute zero pressure, and zero inches of Hg at atmospheric pressure. A vacuum of 29 inches of Hg therefore equals a vacuum of 25 mm Hg.
Minor Vacuum Expressed in inches of water. Often called draft. Thirty inches of water draft corresponds to a vacuum of about two inches of Hg.
Absolute Pressure To avoid confusion, the designer should not use psia in designating equipment requirements. A pressure of 1 psia corresponds to a vacuum of 50 mm Hg or 28 inches of Hg.

▶ Products of thermal cracking of the plant's feed.
▶ Low molecular weight (light) components in the feed.

Too often, the process designer shortcuts the design of the vacuum system by leaving the entire job to an equipment supplier. The inexperienced designer simply summarizes the following information:

▶ Steam pressure and temperature
▶ Cooling water temperature
▶ Desired vacuum
▶ Molecular weight of the tail gas
▶ Anticipated pounds per hour of tail gas

The designer sends this information off to a vacuum system vendor and considers his job done. This fallacy is illustrated by the following incidents.

Steam Pressure Affects Vacuum

The most common way to pull a vacuum is with a steam jet. Figure 10-1 shows a simplified steam jet. The basic principle of operation is:

▶ The pressure head of steam is converted to a velocity head through the steam nozzle.
▶ The high-velocity steam, which develops a very low pressure, sucks in the low-pressure tail gas.
▶ The combined steam plus tail-gas stream slows down and repressurizes in the diffuser. The final pressure is lower than the initial steam pressure, but higher than the initial tail-gas pressure.
▶ The aftercondenser condenses the steam and vents off the tail gas.

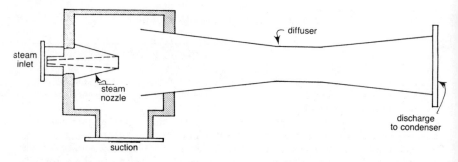

Figure 10-1. The steam nozzle and diffuser in a vacuum jet are custom-designed for each application.

The steam-jet manufacturer can design jets to function over a wide range of steam pressures. This is not to say that he can design a jet to work equally well with varying steam pressures. The jet must be designed to work at a particular steam pressure.

On one unit, the designer knew that the refinery steam pressure would vary between 130 psig and 170 psig. He decided to design the steam jets for 150-psig steam. Aware that the jets performance would suffer at lower steam pressures, he added a spare jet in parallel with the basic steam jets. His idea was to turn on the spare jet whenever the refinery steam pressure dropped below 150 psig.

Unfortunately, steam jets do not work this way. A jet that is designed for 150 psig will gradually draw less vacuum as the steam pressure falls to 140 psig. Below 140 psig, the performance will drop precipitously. On this particular unit, here is what happened:

Steam Pressure (psig)	Vacuum (Inches of Hg)
160	26
150	26
140	25
130	16

The correct way to handle the problem of variable steam pressure to a vacuum system is shown in Figure 10-2. The steam pressure is maintained by throttling the steam through a control valve. A jet designed to use 130-psig steam will consume about 15% more steam than a jet designed to use 150-psig steam.

Why not simply design the jet for 130 psig, save the cost of the control valve shown in Figure 10-2, and reap the benefits of deeper vacuum whenever the steam pressure is higher than design? This approach is false because: (1) a steam jet works best with the design steam pressure, and (2) higher steam pressure forces more steam through the jet; however, the incremental steam flow is wasted and can reduce vacuum.

It is not possible to improve the vacuum of an existing steam jet by superheating the steam supply. Although moisture in the steam to jets will markedly reduce their performance, superheated steam will not help.

Jet Capacity

The amount of vacuum a single jet draws will vary with gas load. This is partially because the flow of steam, which provides the motive force, remains constant regardless of the gas flow, and partially because the jet's diffuser has been designed for a particular gas rate.

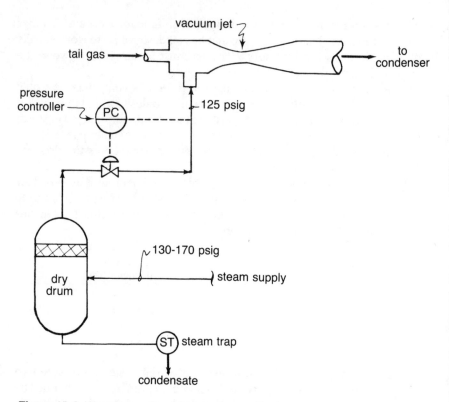

Figure 10-2. Wet steam of variable pressure will ruin a vacuum steam jet's performance.

Figure 10-3 shows the effect on vacuum for a particular single-stage jet discharging to the atmosphere.

Seal Leg Design

The vacuum-jet system—including the jets and condensers—will be designed by the jet vendor. The process engineer must design the seal legs, the seal drum, and determine the condenser elevations. Difficulty arises because the condensers are under vacuum and cannot simply be drained to a sewer. There are two ways to approach this problem: (1) vacuum pumping drums, and (2) full elevation of the condensers.

The simplest method is to locate the condensers high enough so that they will drain by gravity into the seal drum. To calculate this elevation,

$$H_c = 1.1 \ (P_c)$$

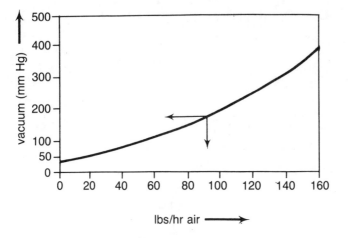

Figure 10-3. Performance curve for a single-stage ejector.

where:
H_c = minimum height of the condenser bottom above the maximum liquid level in the seal pot, feet.
P_c = pressure in the condenser, inches of Hg.

Figure 10-4 illustrates this arrangement. Note that the elevation calculated is not the total elevation of the condenser above grade. The seal drum itself will probably be 15 feet above grade. This will put the jet or precondenser 50 feet above grade. Each subsequent condenser can then be set at a progressively lower elevation. Of course, the other condensers will be much smaller than the precondenser (or first-stage condenser, if there is no precondenser), and so one might as well set all the jets and condensers on the same deck to simplify the piping.[1]

In the "full-elevation condenser method" of sizing seal legs, the seal drum is vented to the atmosphere and will run at a slight positive pressure. Only one seal drum is required, regardless of the number of condensers. On the other hand, with vacuum pumping drums as seal drums, a separate seal drum is required for each condenser, but the entire assembly can be located much closer to grade. Figure 10-5 illustrates this rather complex design. Each seal drum operates at the same pressure as the outlet of the condenser that it serves. This is achieved by means of the equalizing lines shown in Figure 10-5.

The principal disadvantage of this scheme, in addition to requiring multiple seal drums, is that the condensate pump must now be operated with a subatmospheric suction pressure. This can be an operating headache because the condensate pump will cavitate when it has a leaking seal. Note in

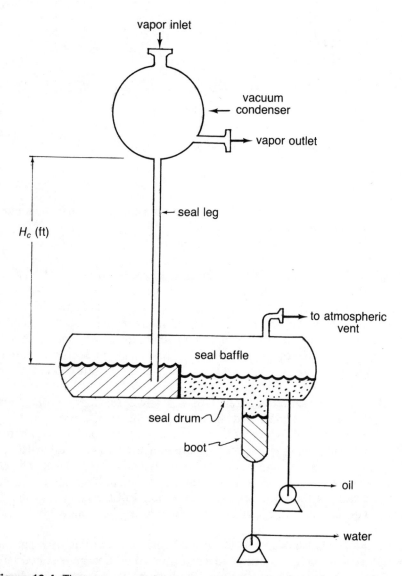

Figure 10-4. The vacuum condenser must be elevated above the seal drum for drainage.

Figure 10-5 that the liquid from the second seal drum is pressured back to the first seal drum. This simplification saves one set of pumps.

Design of Seal Drums

Figure 10-4 shows a properly designed seal drum. The essential features of this drum are:

▶ Any number of seal legs may be run to the same drum. However, seal legs from condensers operating at different pressures must never be joined.
▶ The seal leg must be assembled inside the drum so that it will never leak. This is a rather vital point because once the seal drum is closed, there is no way that the seal leg can be inspected. Figure 10-6 shows the best way to

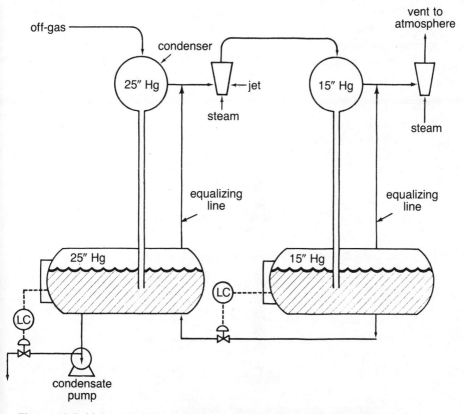

Figure 10-5. Maintaining the seal drums under a vacuum lowers the elevation of the condensers.

solve the problem. The process engineer needs to include this mechanical detail in his design report.

Once I was assigned to determine why a particular vacuum system could not pull its normal vacuum. After weeks of fruitless efforts, we opened the seal drum. There we found that no gaskets had been installed between the seal-leg internal flanges. As the seal drum was operating at atmospheric pressure, air was being sucked up into the seal leg and into the jet system through the leaky flanges. This situation illustrates the need for the bottom internal flange shown in Figure 10-6. Temporarily placing a blank flange over this internal flange allows the entire seal-leg assembly to be fully tested for leaks.

▶ The height of the seal baffle shown in Figure 10-4 above the bottom of the seal leg is not too critical. A typical dimension for this height is 1-2 feet. The volume on the left-hand side of the seal drum shown in Figure 10-4 must be equal to or greater than the combined volume of the seal legs. In case the steam to the jets is accidentally shut off, this will prevent air from being sucked back up into the vacuum system.

▶ The liquid drained out of the condensers overflows the seal baffle into the oil-water separator side of the seal drum. This section of the drum is sized like any other oil-water separator, that is, 7-10 minutes gross residence time based on net water production. A six-inch riser is mandatory for the oil draw-off nozzle.

▶ The drum is vented to the atmosphere, but during normal operation no vapors should be created.

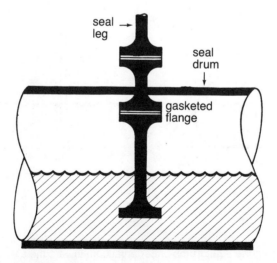

Figure 10-6. The seal leg inside the seal drum must be absolutely leak proof.

An Unfortunate Incident

For three days and three nights we had been trying to start up the world's largest vacuum column. The huge tower, capable of recovering 110,000 barrels per day of gas oil from crude oil residue, was designed to operate at 29 inches of Hg vacuum. The best we could do was 22 inches of Hg.

The unit was equipped, as shown in Figure 10-7, with two parallel trains of steam ejectors. As there was a steam shortage in the refinery, we were only using one of the two trains. This was not felt to be our problem because we could only pull 22 inches of Hg vacuum with absolutely no feed in the unit. Also, we knew that we were not overloading the single train of jets because of an air leak. We could block off the steam to the jets and still hold 20 inches of Hg vacuum for hours.

Remember that one train of steam jets was not in service. With this information, a first-class process designer should be able to solve this problem by studying Figure 10-7. If not, read on.

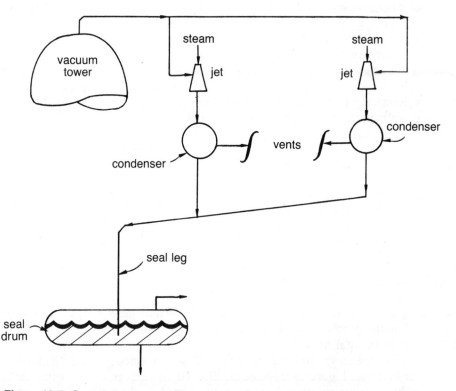

Figure 10-7. Connecting two condenser drains to the same seal leg was a design error.

With both condenser drains tied into the same seal leg at an elevation where the seal leg will not be liquid-filled, vapor from one condenser will recycle to the other condenser backward through the idle jet and then back to the suction of the working jet. This overloads the working jet. This problem only occurred when steam was cut off to one train of jets.

To rectify this problem, block valves were installed immediately below each condenser drain. When the steam to a jet was shut off, the drain line from the condenser, which served the idled jet, was closed off with the new block valve.

Tail-Gas Quantity

The amount of noncondensible gas coming from a vacuum tower is a function of:

▶ *Residence time of the feed in the vacuum feed preheat furnace.* The longer the residence time, the greater the amount of gas generated.
▶ *Characteristics of the feed.* An aromatic-type feed will give off less gas than a paraffinic feed.
▶ *Heater outlet temperature.* For every increase of roughly 20°F, the amount of noncondensible tail gas will double.

Figure 10-8 shows an empirically derived correlation to predict tail-gas volumes per barrel of feed. A typical tail-gas composition for a high-sulfur petroleum residue vacuum tower feed is:

	Mole % (Dry Basis)
H_2	5
N_2	20
O_2	2
CO_2, CO	3
C_1	40
C_2	8
C_3 plus	10
H_2S	12

For certain crude oils, the amount of H_2S in the ejector tail gas will exceed 20 mole percent. Disposal of this stream can therefore be a serious environmental hazard.

For vacuum systems in which no cracking is expected, jet sizing is based on air leakage. Figure 10-9 shows anticipated air leakage for a commercially tight vacuum system.[2] The designer should double this quantity when specifying required jet capacity.

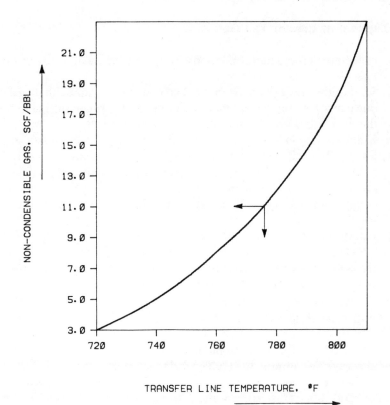

Figure 10-8. Tail-gas rates from the vacuum distillation of petroleum residue.

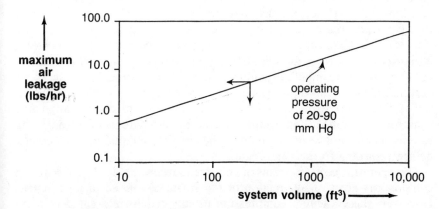

Figure 10-9. Air leakage into vacuum systems for sizing jets.

Disposal of Ejector Tail Gas

There are three general methods to dispose of vacuum tower off-gas:

▶ Vent to the atmosphere from the final condenser. Although illegal, since one cannot routinely vent hydrocarbons and hydrogen sulfide to the air, this is a widespread practice.
▶ Compress the tail gas, either with a liquid seal ring compressor or steam jet, and burn the gas via a low-pressure burner in a process heater. This method will work if the tail gas is diluted with regular fuel gas. However, attempts to burn the tail gas alone will result in plugged burner tips. The oxygen and hydrogen sulfide will react in the presence of moisture to form solid sulfur.
▶ Educt the tail gas with fuel gas into a burner in a process heater. Using 60-100-psig fuel gas as the motive gas, instead of steam in a jet, will save the cost of the steam and dilute the tail gas. This is the simplest and hence the preferred method of disposing of tail gas.

Liquid Seal Ring Compressors

An excellent alternative to pulling a vacuum with a steam jet is to use a liquid seal ring compressor. I have used these machines to pull a vacuum of 20 inches of Hg on a large vacuum tower. The compressor simultaneously developed enough discharge pressure to exhaust the vacuum tail gas through a burner and into a firebox.

Figure 10-10 illustrates the major components of a Graham[3] liquid seal ring compressor. The pump case is half-filled with water or diesel oil. The liquid is thrown to the periphery of the casing and forms a liquid ring which seals the space between the impeller blades and the casing. At the top position of the impeller, the chambers between the impeller blades are filled with liquid. As the eccentric impeller rotates, the liquid ring moves away from the hub, increasing the space in the pumping chamber. This draws gas into the chamber from the inlet port next to the impeller. As the impeller revolves, gas in the impeller chambers is compressed by the liquid ring and is expelled through the outlet port.

The liquid inside the case also absorbs the heat of condensation and compression. Hence, liquid must be continuously circulated through the case by means of an external pump. The circulating liquid must be cooled before returning to the compressor.

The operating costs, in terms of energy requirements, for liquid seal ring compressors are a small fraction of the steam consumed in jet ejectors. However, these vacuum compressors usually require a great deal more maintenance than do steam jets. Also, they are relatively tricky to operate.

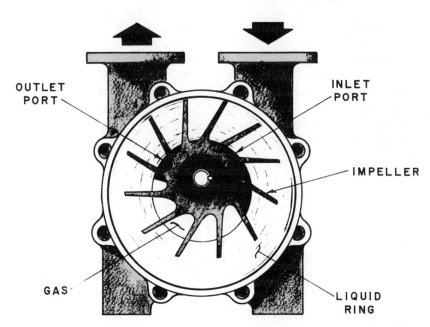

OUTLET PORT

INLET PORT

IMPELLER

GAS

LIQUID RING

Figure 10-10. Liquid seal-ring vacuum pump. (Courtesy Graham Manufacturing Co., Inc.)

For instance, the rate of liquid circulation through the compressor case must be precisely set. Too little liquid flow will lead to low compressor efficiency; too much flow can cause the eccentric impeller to bog down·and result in equipment damage.

On balance, a liquid seal ring compressor should be used in preference to a steam-jet ejector when the following conditions prevail:

► The compressor is located in an area where it can be frequently checked by operations personnel.
► In large applications, which ordinarily require several thousand pounds per hour of steam if jets are used.
► Steam for vacuum jets is costly or in short supply.

Finally, do not specify liquid seal ring vacuum compressors to save energy and then include a backup steam jet in the design. Whenever I have seen this done, the operators used the zero-maintenance steam jet and abandoned the compressor as requiring excessive maintenance. Use the same philosophy for a liquid ring machine as for any centrifugal pump in critical service—provide a 100% spare.

References

1. Neild, A. B. and Osbourne, A., eds., *Modern Marine Engineer's Manual*, 2nd ed., Cornell Maritime Press, Inc. Cambridge, Maryland, 1965.
2. "Air Leakage in Commercially Tight Vacuum Systems," Schutte & Koerting Co., Bulletin 5E.
3. "Graham Liquid Ring Vacuum Pumps, Principle of Operation," Graham Vacuum & Heat Transfer Manufacturing Co., Inc.

11

Centrifugal Compressors: Designing to Avoid Surge

All that is best in mechanical, metallurgical, and structural science goes into the design of centrifugal machines. Yet, unless the process engineer correctly specifies the duty of the compressor and properly integrates it into the plant's control scheme, the centrifugal compressor will never function properly in spite of its mechanical assets.

There are two general classes of compressors: positive displacement, and dynamic. A centrifugal compressor is a dynamic machine because it achieves its compression by applying and converting inertial forces. The positive displacement compressor—such as a reciprocating machine—compresses gas by direct volume reduction.[1]

Reciprocating Compressors

A compression job that requires 100 kilowatts of power to perform with a centrifugal compressor can be done with 80 kilowatts by a reciprocating compressor. Reciprocating machines, especially for smaller applications of less than 1000-2000 acfm (actual cubic feet per minute of gas to the suction of the compressor) are far more efficient than centrifugal compressors. However, operating personnel prefer centrifugal compressors because they require far less maintenance than reciprocating compressors. Most frequently, the valves on a reciprocating machine's cylinders—which must open and close with each cycle—are subject to sticking and a host of other mechanical failures. Whenever the process gas is dirty or can precipitate deposits such as ammonium chloride, use of reciprocating compressors will lead to a maintenance nightmare.

For applications above 3000 acfm, a centrifugal compressor is more cost effective than a reciprocating machine.

Centrifugal Compressor Characteristics

A motor-driven centrifugal compressor will operate at a constant speed. The constant-speed feature, along with several other intrinsic characteristics, result in a lack of flexibility in the centrifugal machine. The most infamous restrictive characteristic is "surge."

Below a certain acfm suction volume, a centrifugal compressor will enter an operating range where its performance becomes unstable. The minimum suction volume required to prevent a compressor from surging is different for each machine.

What Is Surge?

Compressor vendors supply a performance curve with each machine, as shown in Figure 11-1. When the acfm that the compressor is pumping falls to the left of the surge point shown in Figure 11-1, the rotor (i.e., that part of the compressor that is spinning) begins to slide back and forth across its radial bearings. The end of the compressor shaft hits the thrust bearing (i.e., the component that constrains the axial movement of the rotor). Each movement of the shaft against the thrust bearings is called a surge. Depending on the speed of the compressor and its mechanical strength, it can withstand 100-2000 surges before the thrust bearing is damaged and the

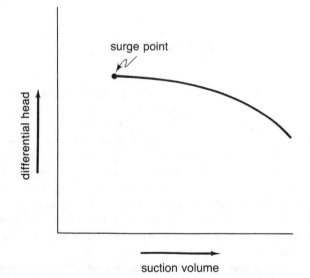

Figure 11-1. A centrifugal compressor back-up on its curve to the left of the surge point will self-destruct.

compressor self-destructs. In general, the slower the speed of a compressor, the more insensitive it is to surging. A speed of 3000 rpm is quite slow for a centrifugal machine, while 10,000 rpm is extremely fast.

What Causes Surge

A particular centrifugal machine may be thrown into surge by a number of process changes of the fluid being compressed, such as reduced molecular weight, higher suction temperature, lower suction pressure, and higher discharge pressure.

Also, for a variable-speed machine, reducing the rpm can precipitate surge.

The key idea to grasp in understanding the cause of surge is that a centrifugal compressor develops a fixed *polytropic head* which is a function of its mechanical characteristics, the volume of gas being pumped, and its speed—but not the physical properties of the gas being compressed. We, as process engineers, are not interested in a concept such as polytropic head; we want to know that the compressor will deliver a certain discharge pressure with a given suction pressure. Polytropic head is related to pressure rise as follows:

$$P_D - P_S \simeq D \times H_p$$

where:
P_D = discharge pressure.
P_S = suction pressure.
D = density of gas being compressed.
H_p = polytropic head.

In most process applications the discharge pressure of a compressor is fixed independently of the compressor. Suppose that for a constant-speed machine the molecular weight of the fluid being compressed is suddenly reduced by increasing the percent of hydrogen in the feed gas. The compressor must now deliver a greater polytropic head to overcome the same discharge pressure with a lower-density gas. The only way the compressor can develop more polytropic head at a fixed speed is to pump less gas. This means the acfm suction volume decreases. As shown in Figure 11-1 the compressor will reach its surge point at a certain minimum suction volume. The rotor will begin to slide back and forth on its radial bearings, and the machine will make a frightening asthmatic sound.

Other than decreased molecular weight, the other factors that result in lower-density gas are high temperature and low pressure. These, of course, are the same parameters that promote surge.

Variable Molecular Weight

The chances are excellent that a centrifugal compressor designed to handle 30 molecular-weight gas will not be able to compress 20 molecular-weight gas. The pressure differential that the compressor will put up will be reduced by one-third with the lower molecular-weight gas. Up to a point, the compressor will compensate for this by pumping less gas, then the machine will drop into an unstable area and begin to surge. It must then be shutdown to preserve its bearings from destruction.

The process engineer must be quite careful that he does not specify too high a molecular weight for a centrifugal compressor. Why not play it safe and specify a very low molecular weight? Then, in case the molecular weight is higher than design, the excess discharge pressure can always be dissipated across a control valve located downstream of the compressor. Unfortunately, this results in a tremendous waste of energy and an unnecessary mechanical stress on a compressor's rotating assembly.

Compression Work

More technical people seemed confused over the relationship of the total pounds of gas being compressed to the work required than any other common subject. But the relationship is very simple—compression work is proportional to molecular weight.

The most convenient way to express the formula for compression work, in so far as the process designer is concerned, is

$$\text{horsepower} = \left(\frac{P_1 V_1}{33{,}000} \right) \times \left(\frac{K}{K-1} \right) \left[\left(\frac{P_2}{P_1} \right)^{\frac{K-1}{K}} - 1 \right]$$

where:
P_1 = suction pressure, psia.
V_1 = acfm (actual cubic feet per minute suction volume).
K = ratio of specific heats for material being compressed.
P_2 = discharge pressure, psia.

In the previous formula the volume of gas appears, which is a function of the number of moles and other intrinsic properties of the fluid being compressed (compressibility, temperature, and pressure). The molecular weight or total pounds of gas does *not* appear. The fallacy that is believed by many technical people, that compressor horsepower requirements are proportional to the weight of the gas being compressed, arises from the following facts:

▶ An existing compressor operating at a fixed speed and fixed suction volume will deliver a fixed polytropic head regardless of the molecular weight of the gas.
▶ Doubling the molecular weight of the gas will increase the amount of work required because the discharge pressure increases. The fact that a greater weight of gas is being compressed is incidental.

To emphasize the point, recall that compression work for a reciprocating machine is proportional to the number of moles handled. A reciprocating compressor delivers a constant discharge pressure, whereas the centrifugal compressor delivers a higher discharge pressure with an increased molecular weight.

Practical Problems of Variable Molecular Weight

The effects of the process engineer specifying the wrong molecular weight in his design manifest themselves in the field in two ways:

▶ *Molecular weight lower than design.* The compressor cannot develop enough discharge pressure. The compressor's motor drive pulls less amperage, and less gas volume is pumped as the molecular weight drops. Finally, the acfm may fall below a critical point and the compressor will start surging.
▶ *Molecular weight higher than design.* The compressor develops too much pressure differential. If its discharge pressure is not artificially raised (for example, with a control valve), the machine's suction pressure will be pulled down. The compressor's motor will pull more amperage and may trip off due to overload. The mechanical stress on the wheels which make up the compressor rotor will increase. Depending on the mechanical strength of these wheels, they may fail due to the extra load they bear because of the higher molecular weight.

Adjusting for Low Molecular Weights

The purpose of the foregoing discussion is not to imply that the process designer must exactly calculate the correct molecular for each service. The reality of process plant operation is too variable to achieve such a degree of exactitude. Rather, the idea is to provide a method of adjusting the molecular weight at the suction of the compressor.

For one large hydrocracker, the molecular weight of the hydrogen-rich makeup gas was adjusted by injecting liquid butane into the compressor suction. Adding 1 mole of butane to 10 moles of the hydrogen-rich gas increased its molecular weight from 8 to 13. The reduced suction temperature caused by the vaporization of the liquid butane also increased the suction density of the gas being handled. In this way the differential pressure developed by the centrifugal compressor was doubled with less than a 10% increase in moles of gas compressed.

A rather less efficient, but more common, method of dealing with the problem of low molecular-weight gas is to heat the compressor suction drum. This energy-intensive method is illustrated in Figure 11-2. Note that the average molecular weight of the incremental moles vaporized in this way may not be that much greater than the molecular weight of the fluid being compressed. Also, heating the suction gas decreases its density, which has the opposite effect of increasing the molecular weight. Before assuming that this method will work in controlling molecular weight, the process designer should carry out a series of equilibrium flash vaporization calculations at various temperatures for the drum shown in Figure 11-2.

Maximum Number of Wheels

There is no practical way to compress pure hydrogen from 100 psig to 3000 psig in a single centrifugal compressor. The very low molecular weight, combined with the high pressure ratio means that a huge polytropic head is required. As each of the wheels on a centrifugal compressor can put up a

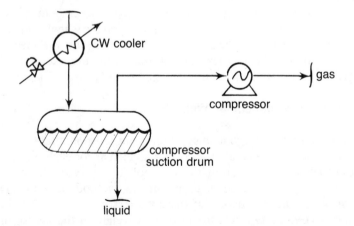

Figure 11-2. Raising the temperature of the suction drum will increase the density of the gas being compressed.

limited polytropic head, the number of wheels required results in an impossibly long rotor.

The answer to this quandary is to raise the molecular weight artificially. The case of butane injection just described is a typical industrial example and emphasizes the need for close communication between the process designer and the mechanical engineer responsible for compressor selection.

Allowing for High Molecular Weight

Electric motors are relatively inexpensive when compared to other process plant equipment. Also, an oversized electric motor will not draw any more power than a motor barely large enough for the application. For these reasons, the electric drive on a centrifugal compressor should be generously sized. The horsepower rating of the motor should be oversized in direct proportion to the maximum expected molecular weight of the fluid handled. For example, if a 2000-hp motor is required to handle a design molecular weight of 40, then a 2500-hp electric driver should be purchased if the maximum expected molecular weight can reach 50. Of course, the mechanical strength of the rotor must also be beefed up in the same proportion.

Suction Throttling

I spent 10 years as a process designer and field engineer before I understood the necessity of locating a control valve on the suction of a centrifugal compressor. It was not until I observed an ancient, gray-bearded chief operator manually throttling the suction to a compressor in a unit that I designed that my error became transparent.

A compressor developing too much head may be throttled either on the suction or discharge. However, controlling the compressor discharge pressure by throttling on the suction side only wastes half as much horsepower as would be lost by restricting the discharge flow. The hoary chief operator knew this. He was pinching back on the compressor suction to reduce amperage on the compressor's electric-motor drive. If only for start-up purposes, when large electric motors can pull excessive amperage due to high initial starting torque, one should provide a control valve on the compressor suction.

Figure 11-3 shows how to design a compressor for maximum energy waste and, consequently, maximum stress on the rotor's components. If the designer provides a suction throttling control valve, the safety factors discussed in the previous section (i.e., rotor stress and motor sizing) may be reduced by half.

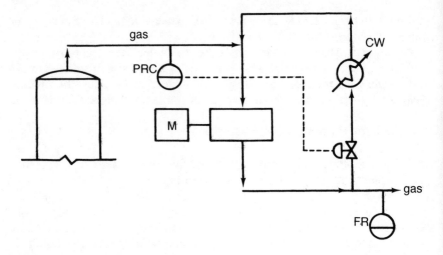

Figure 11-3. A motor-driven centrifugal compressor must have a suction control valve. The spill-back control pictured will not protect the motor from overamping.

References

1. Ingersoll-Rand, *Turbo Sales Manual,* Section 201, September 6, 1974.
2. Lapina, R. P., *Estimating Centrifugal Compressor Performance,* Process Compressor Technology, Vol. 1, Gulf Publishing Co., 1982, Chapter 7.

12

Sizing Centrifugal Pumps

The centrifugal pump is the workhorse for moving liquids in a refinery. Figure 12-1 shows the major working components of a typical centrifugal pump.

Liquid is pressured into the suction of the pump where the impeller imparts a centrifugal velocity to the fluid. As the liquid discharges from the pump, its velocity head is converted to pressure head.

The process design engineer must consider two characteristics of centrifugal pumps: their discharge pressure, and volumetric flow rate. The designer's heat and material balance will dictate the required flow rate, and hydraulic calculations will indicate the head.

How Much Head Is Required?

Figure 12-2 illustrates a typical process application. In this sketch the required head consists of five components:

▶ Differential pressure between the two vessels.
▶ Head to lift the liquid.
▶ Friction head loss in the piping.
▶ Pressure drop allowed to control the flow.
▶ NPSH for the pump.

To calcuate the differential pressure in head between the two vessels, the following formula is used:

$$\text{head (ft)} = \frac{\text{differential pressure} \times 2.31}{\text{sp gr}}$$

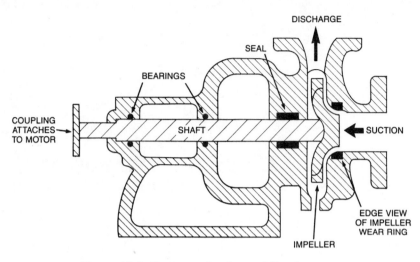

Figure 12-1. Components of a centrifugal pump.

where sp gr is the specific gravity of the liquid pumped at the process temperature. Figure 12-3 shows how to correct specific gravity for temperature.

The head to lift the liquid is simply the difference between the liquid level in the first vessel and the level at which the pump discharge reaches a vapor space.

As the process design engineer does not normally lay out the piping configuration, how can he estimate the friction head loss in the piping? Just assume that the piping designer will allow one psi pressure drop for each 100 feet of piping. Then estimate the approximate distance the piping will run. Double the calculated pressure drop to allow for elbows, valves, and other fittings in the piping. Next, convert the friction pressure drop to feet of head.

The pressure drop allowed for the control valve should be computed as the greater of 20 psi or 50% of the anticipated piping friction loss.

The NPSH for a pump is given in the manufacturer's pump curve and is usually 5-15 feet. In summary, the total pump head requirement for Figure 12-2 is

$$\text{total head} = \underbrace{\frac{(100-20) \times 2.31}{.78}}_{\text{(pressure rise)}} + \underbrace{(60-20)}_{\text{(vert. ht.)}} + \underbrace{2 \times \frac{400}{100} \times \frac{2.31}{.78}}_{\text{(friction loss)}}$$

$$+ \underbrace{\frac{20 \times 2.31}{.78}}_{\text{(cont. valve)}} + \underbrace{8}_{\text{(NPSH)}} = 372 \text{ feet}$$

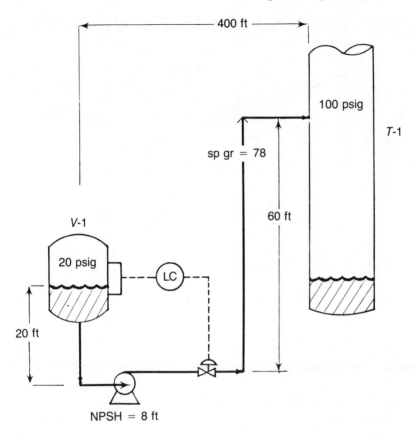

Figure 12-2. Calculating the head required for a centrifugal pump.

Some engineers like to "play it safe" and allow a large excess in pressure drop for the control valve. This is a bad design practice, as the control valve will then usually operate in a mostly closed position and result in poor level or flow control characteristics.

How Much Flow Is Required?

The pounds per hour of liquid to be pumped is calculated from the heat and material balance. The pump gpm is then calculated by

$$\text{gpm} = \frac{\text{lbs/hr}}{500 \times \text{sp gr}}$$

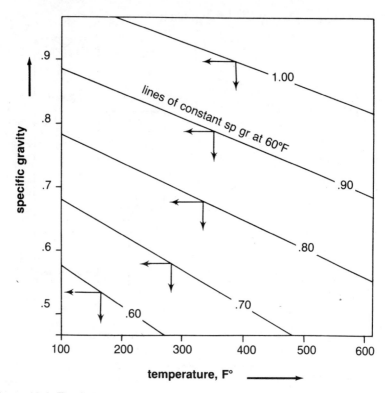

Figure 12-3. The fluid density used in pump calculations must be corrected for the process temperature.

For example, if one has to pump 60,000 pounds per hour of gasoline (which has a specific gravity of 0.80 at 60°F) at a temperature of 300°F, the required gpm is

$$\frac{60,000}{500 \times .67} = 180 \text{ gpm}$$

Selecting a Pump's Impeller

Figure 12-1 shows the arrangement of an impeller inside a pump case. The size of the impeller determines the amount of flow and head delivered by the pump. Impeller sizes can be varied widely for centrifugal pumps.

Figure 12-4 shows a typical set of pump curves. Each curve represents the characteristics of an individual impeller. The top curve is for the largest-size impeller that can physically fit into the pump. Impellers are easily machined for any intermediate size between those indicated on the pump curve.

The manufacturer will supply a set of curves for each type they sell. Never select a pump which requires the maximum-size impeller. When put in service, you may find the impeller selected is too small. If this happens, it is quite inexpensive to install a larger impeller ($100-$1000). To install a larger pump is a major project ($10,000-$100,000).

When choosing an impeller size, do not forget start-up conditions. Perhaps the pump must put up 50% more head to establish initial circulation than is required during normal operation.

Selecting a Pump's Motor

An experienced process designer will usually select a motor for a centrifugal pump based *not* on the size of the impeller that is used, but on the largest-size impeller that will fit into the pump. There are two good reasons for this selection.

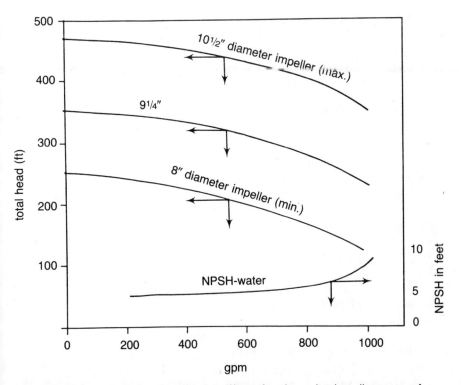

Figure 12-4. Pump curve showing the effect of various size impellers on performance.

First, the larger motor will make it easier for operating personnel to start the pump, as the motor will be less likely to trip on high initial starting torque. Note that the electrical current drawn by a motor is a function of the head and flow put out by the pump and is *not* proportional to the motor's rated horsepowers.

Second, some clever field engineer will sooner or later want to expand the pump's capacity by changing the impeller to a larger size.

Shut-In Pressure

The shut-in pressure is the pressure the pump will put up at zero flow. The vertical, left-hand axis on Figure 12-4 shows the shut-in pressure for various-size impellers. The larger the impeller, the higher the shut-in pressure.

The maximum allowable shut-in pressure is a critical variable when selecting the size of an impeller. The process designer can be assured that eventually an operator will block in a pump downstream of a heat exchanger or vessel.

Figure 12-5 illustrates the problem. If an operator accidentally closes valve 1, the shell of heat exchanger E-1 will be subject to the full shut-in pump discharge pressure. If the heat exchanger's shell can stand the pump's shut-in pressure, then there is no problem. However, if the shell is not designed for the pump's shut-in pressure, the designer has three options:

▶ Use a smaller impeller.
▶ Install a relief valve on the shell (an expensive and messy proposition).
▶ Eliminate valve 1.

Too often, the process designer ignores the consequences to downstream equipment when expanding a pump's capacity by enlarging the impeller. The need to design all process equipment between a pump and a block valve for the pump's shut-in pressure is a legal requirement.

Expanding Pumping Capacity

There are two inexpensive methods to expand pumping capacity: (1) reduce downstream pressure drop, and (2) increase the size of the pump's impeller.

Reducing Hydraulic Bottlenecks

A pressure survey conducted by a trained technical man is usually the most cost-effective way of expanding pumping capacity. A single pressure

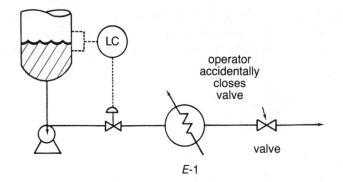

Figure 12-5. Oversizing pump impellers can overpressure downstream equipment.

gauge is moved from the pump discharge, and successive pressure readings are taken between pieces of process equipment. Sections of the plant giving high pressure drop are thus defined. Table 12-1 indicates typical causes of excessive pressure drop and suggested remedies.

Larger Impeller

The trick to selecting a larger impeller when expanding a pump's capacity is to match the impeller size to the capacity of the existing motor drive. The

Table 12-1
Reducing Pressure Drops

Cause	Modification
1. High tube-side pressure drop through a shell-and-tube heat exchanger.	Reduce the number of tube-side passes. Going from four passes to two passes cuts pressure drop by ⅞s.
2. High shell-side pressure drop through a shell-and-tube heat exchanger.	A new tube bundle with larger spaces between the baffles is required. This is expensive ($50,000 for a large bundle).
3. High pressure drop through a wide open control valve.	Change the control valve "port size" or "trim" to the maximum size permitted in the control valve body. For instance, a 3-inch control valve can accommodate a 2¼-inch port size.
4. Excessive piping losses. (More than 1 psi per 100 equivalent feet).	Increase diameter of piping or parallel piping runs.
5. Mix valve pressure drop.	For most services (oil and water) a pressure drop of 10-20 psig is adequate for good mixing.

impeller itself will be cheap and easy to install; replacing the motor and its associated electrical components will be a costly proposition.

The effect on changing the diameter of an impeller is approximated as follows:

$$Q_2 = Q_1 \, (d_2/d_1)$$
$$h_2 = h_1 \, (d_2/d_1)^2$$
$$A_2 = A_1 \, (d_2/d_1)^3$$

where:

Q_2 = flow rate with larger impeller.
Q_1 = flow rate with existing impeller.
d_2 = diameter of larger impeller.
d_1 = diameter of existing impeller.
h_2 = head delivered by larger impeller.
h_1 = head delivered by existing impeller.
A_2 = amperage drawn by motor with larger impeller.
A_1 = amperage drawn by motor with existing impeller.

To decide on the maximum-size impeller that can be used with the existing motor, it is best to make the following field measurements:

▶ Place the pumps discharge control valve in a wide-open position.
▶ Measure the amperage drawn by the pump.

The rated capacity of the motor (in amps) can be multiplied by its service factor (typically 10% or 15%). To calculate the maximum-size impeller that can be used with the existing motor, find

$$d_2 = d_1 \, (Ar/A_1)^{1/3}$$

where Ar is the rated amperage of the motor, including its service factor.

Correct Process Design Minimizes Pump Maintenance

Once a process pump is commissioned and operating successfully, there are only two significant causes of future failures: (1) loss of NPSH, and (2) low discharge flow.

When a centrifugal pump's discharge is closed, it will overheat. The motor's electrical power is converted to heat as the pump churns the trapped liquid. The pump's case and bearings become hotter and hotter. Eventually, the bearings will burn out and damage the pump's seal. In addition, many large high-head centrifugal pumps are subject to a phenomenon called "internal recirculation" which damages the pumps internal parts when the pump is operated at reduced rates.

A simple process modification, as shown in Figure 12-6, will automatically prevent pump damage due to low flow. The designer should consider whether the minimum flow by-pass shown in figure 12-6 is necessary considering the process variables of the plant designed. Do not tie the minimum flow discharge line into the suction of the pump. This defeats the purpose of the line; it must be routed back to a point in the process where the pumping heat energy can be dissipated.

Protecting Against Low NPSH

When a centrifugal pump loses suction due to insufficient NPSH, the pumped fluid begins to flash at the eye of the implier. The resulting bubbles of vapor are compressed and collapse as the mixed-phase fluid passes through the impeller. This is called cavitation and is easily the most common cause of pump failure in a process plant.

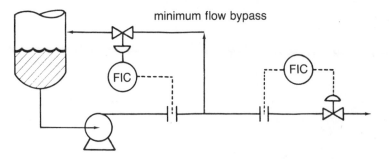

Figure 12-6. Equipment shown in dark is needed to prevent the pump from over-heating at low flow rates.

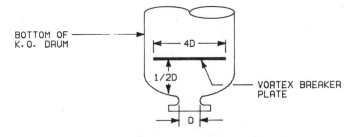

Figure 12-7. Vortex breaker design.

A designer can prevent damage to many pumps by applying a few simple ideas:

▶ Locate coolers on the suction side of pumps. The decreased pump suction pressure will usually be more than offset by the reduction in the fluid's bubble point.
▶ Provide vortex breakers in the bottom of all vessels, regardless of the anticipated liquid level in the vessel (see figure 12-7 for a suggested vortex-breaker design).
▶ Provide adequate liquid hold time in process vessels acting as surge drums. A net liquid hold time of 5-15 minutes is a typical range.

13

Shell-and-Tube
Heat Exchangers—The Pitfalls
of Oversizing

Quietly, and without rancor, I entered the crowded meeting room. Everyone in the refinery was there, and as the latecomer I stood in the doorway. My clothes were covered with tar, so although it was uncomfortable to stand, it was better. Bill Ceels, who designed the system to cool the petroleum residue (tar) from our new vacuum distillation unit, sat at the far end of the room. Neat and organized, unlit pipe in his teeth, he avoided my eyes.

The residue cooling system had cost $2 million to build. It consisted of eight large shell-and-tube heat exchangers arranged for parallel flow. Constructed to outlast the rest of the refinery, it was the pride of the mechanical engineering department. Dazzling metallic in its new insulation, the cooling system had only one drawback—it could not cool the residue. Bill Ceels, the process designer who created the system, could not, would not, acknowledge its failure.

For two weeks we had dueled over the question; I, the field engineer, insisting that the heat exchangers would never work, and Bill, the designer, equally adamant that his design would be a success. Finally, out of frustration, the refinery manager had called this meeting to settle the question.

I had deliberately worn my residue-soaked clothes to the meeting as a mute testament to the honest effort expended to make the exchangers work. Standing silently, I listened to Bill's soft, well-formed words explain the computer output that had formed the basis for the residue cooling system design. His ordered logic and self-confidence quickly overwhelmed my mumbled retorts. Nodding in agreement, the refinery manager turned to me, leaned back in his heavy leather chair and lit his pipe.

"Three feet per second" was all I could say, "Not less than three feet per second." Embarrassed by my inarticulateness, I turned and left.

Three Feet Per Second

Figure 13-1 shows the configuration of a shell-and-tube exchanger.[1] Some of parameters for the process designer to set are:

▶ Which fluid is on the shell side, and which fluid is on the tube side.
▶ Shell-side fluid velocity (normally not less than 3 fps).
▶ Shell-and-tube-side fouling coefficients (that is, quantifying how much dirt sticking to the tubes will reduce the heat-transfer coefficient).
▶ Tube pitch.
▶ Tube baffle spacing and "cut." (see Figure 13-4)
▶ Tube diameter.

The critical parameter in designing heat-exchange equipment is always velocity. Low velocities lead to poor heat-transfer coefficients, accelerated rates of fouling and, for high-viscosity fluids, plugging of the heat exchanger.

There is no exact guideline for minimum velocity. Certainly, the designer should try to keep velocities in the turbulent flow range, rather than in the laminar flow range. This means the Renolds number must be *above* 2100. A general rule of thumb is to keep velocities on both the shell-and-tube sides of a heat exchanger above 3 fps and below 10 fps.

High velocities (above 10 fps) lead to excessive rates of erosion-corrosion of metal surfaces. Low velocities encourage particulate matter to stick to the tubes.

Calculating Tube-Side Velocity

The tube-side velocity is calculated by dividing the number of tubes by the number of passes that the tube-side fluid makes in going through the tube bundle. This is the number of tubes per pass. The tube-side flow is then divided by the number of tubes per pass to arrive at the tube-side velocity.

But suppose the previous exercise yields a velocity of only 1 fps? Is this OK? Certainly the heat-transfer coefficient will be reduced

$$U \simeq V^{0.7}$$

where:
U = heat-transfer coefficient, Btu/hr/ft^2/°F
V = fluid velocity, fps.

The inexperienced process designer, or for that matter the senior man who has never ventured onto a process unit, may argue that the low velocity can simply be compensated for with increased surface area according to

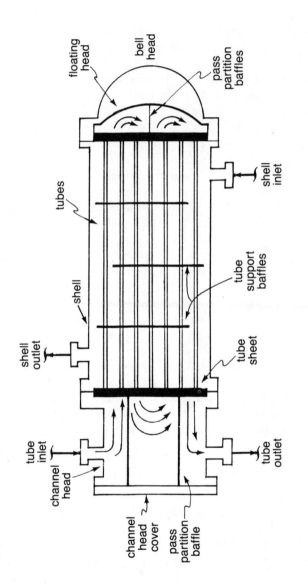

Figure 13-1. Diagram of a four-pass, floating-head, shell-and-tube heat exchanger. Note the indicated direction of tube-side flow.

$$Q = U \times A \times \Delta T$$

where:

Q = exchanger duty, Btu/hr.

A = exchanger heat-transfer surface, ft²

ΔT = temperature difference between the shell-and-tube-side fluids, °F.

This was the argument that Bill advanced in his design of the residue cooling system described at the start of this chapter: "Low velocities lead to low heat-transfer coefficients which may be compensated by increased heat-transfer surface." This is dead wrong. Low velocities lead to fouling and plugging for which no amount of heat-exchanger surface area is going to compensate.

For high-viscosity fluids, as in the case of Mr. Ceels residue coolers, the residue froze up and plugged the tubes in the coolers when operating velocities were below 1 fps. Even when the exchanger was not plugged, heat transfer was deficient because of high wall viscosities

$$U \simeq \left(\frac{u_i}{u_w}\right)^{.14}$$

where:

u_i = viscosity of the bulk fluid.

u_w = viscosity of the fluid at the tube wall.

When cooling a viscous liquid with water, the temperature at the tube wall will be quite close to the cooling-water temperature *if the tube-side velocity is low*. Although the ratio of the viscosities raised to the 0.14 power typically has a negligible effect on the overall heat-transfer coefficient, if the viscosity is 1 million centistokes (as it is for 100°F petroleum residue), the effect will be large.

How to Design for High Tube-Side Velocity

We eventually modified Mr. Ceels's design from eight exchangers in parallel to four parallel trains—two exchangers in series per train. This doubled the tube-side velocity, but also increased the tube-side pressure drop by a factor of eight. The eight-fold increase in pressure drop was caused by both the flow length and velocity being doubled

$$\Delta P \simeq (V)^2 (L)$$

where:
ΔP = pressure drop.
L = flow-pass length.

Another way to alter the velocity is to change the number of tube passes. Figure 13-2 shows how the tube-side velocity may be doubled in a single heat exchanger by going from two passes to four passes. Of course, this modification will also increase pressure drop by a factor of eight. By altering the pass partitions in the channel head and floating head (see Figure 13-1), the number of tube-side passes can be changed to any number desired.

Returning to Mr. Ceels project, why did he choose to line the eight exchanger shells up in parallel, rather than in a series arrangement? Figure 13-3 tells the story (only two of the eight exchanger shells shown). To avoid the high pressure drop associated with putting exchangers in series and the consequent requirement for a booster pump, Bill chose the low-velocity, low pressure drop design shown on the left-hand side of Figure 13-3.

Single-stage centrifugal pumps for the service shown in Figure 13-3 are relatively low-cost items to purchase and install. Certainly the process designer must never compromise on obtaining a decent exchanger velocity or Renolds number to save pressure drop.

Calculating Shell-Side Velocity

Viscous liquids, fluids with a tendency to plug or those that contain large quantities of dirt, should be placed on the shell side of an exchanger. With only a given amount of pressure to dissipate through an exchanger, one does better in regard to heat transfer by placing the viscous, dirty liquid on the shell side. The basis for this statement is several field tests conducted with hot petroleum residue cooled with water. The tube-side and shell-side services were reversed, and in every case better heat transfer was obtained with the hot residue on the shell side. One suspects that the frequent reversals in direction of the liquid induced by the baffles, as shown in Figure 13-4, promoted turbulence. This turbulence reduced the tendency of a stagnant oil film to build up around the outside of the tubes.

It is much easier to design for a particular velocity on the shell side than on the tube side of an exchanger. For an exchanger of fixed size, the tube-side velocity might be:

Number of Passes	Velocity (fps)
2	1.6
4	3.2
6	4.8
8	6.4

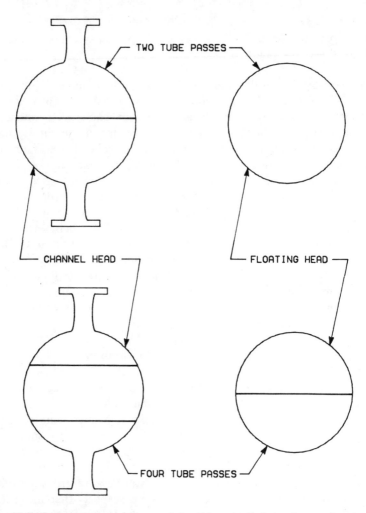

Figure 13-2. An easy way to increase tube side velocity is to change the channel and floating-head pass partitions.

There is no practical way to design for a velocity of, say, 4.2 fps on the tube side. On the shell side, by changing the baffle spacing, any velocity may be obtained.

Although the principal purpose of the baffles is to support the tubes (an unsupported length of more than four feet is excessive and can lead to mechanical failure of the tubes), the baffles also serve an important process function.

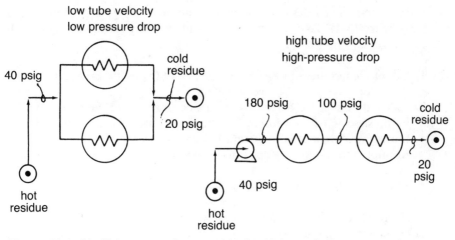

low tube velocity
low pressure drop

high tube velocity
high-pressure drop

40 psig

cold
residue

20 psig

180 psig   100 psig

cold
residue

40 psig

20
psig

hot
residue

hot
residue

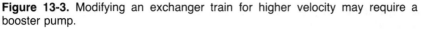

Figure 13-3. Modifying an exchanger train for higher velocity may require a booster pump.

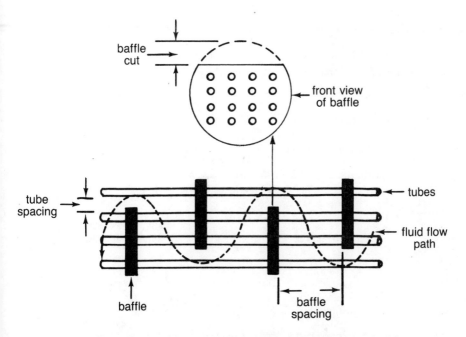

baffle
cut

front view
of baffle

tube
spacing

tubes

fluid flow
path

baffle

baffle
spacing

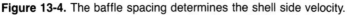

Figure 13-4. The baffle spacing determines the shell side velocity.

By placing the baffles closer together, the shell-side velocity is increased (see Figure 13-4). To calculate the shell-side velocity for square-tube pitch exchangers:

1. Count the number of tubes along the line of the baffle cut and along the diameter. Average the two numbers.
2. Calculate the space between the outside diameter of the tubes and the baffle spacing (do not forget to subtract the baffle thickness). Multiply these two dimensions to obtain the cross-flow area per tube.
3. Multiply the results of steps 1 and 2 together. This is the total crossflow area.
4. Divide the fluid flow by the cross-flow area.

The baffle cut for liquid flow, as shown in Figure 13-4, should be 20-25% of the shell inside diameter. Using a 45% baffle cut to save pressure drop creates stagnant areas in the shell and invalidates the preceding calculation method.[1]

The proper shell-side velocity for most applications is 3-5 fps. The process designer should view with a jaundiced eye velocities falling outside this range.

Always insist that the following TEMA[2] clearances are provided:

▶ The baffle OD to the shell ID (See Table 13-1).
▶ The tube OD to the baffle tube hole ID is 1/64 inch.

Table 13-1
Standard Cross Baffle and Support Plate Clearances
(All Dimensions in Inches)

Nominal Shell ID	Design ID of Shell Minus Baffle OD
6-13	0.100
14-17	0.125
18-23	0.150
24-39	0.175
40-54	0.225
55-60	0.300

(Adapted from *Standards of Tubular Exchanger Manufacturers Association*, 6th edition, 1978.)

Larger clearances than those specified by TEMA permit excessive by-passing around the cross-flow area and thus reduce the effective shell-side velocity.

The big disadvantage of placing the dirty fluid on the shell side of an exchanger is that it is more difficult to clean encrusted deposits from the shell side than from the tube side. It is hard to get at the dirt hidden in the spaces between the tubes; also, the tube bundle must be pulled out of the shell for cleaning. Dirt on the tube side can be simply hydroblasted out after the floating head and channel cover are removed.

If the anticipated deposits can be chemically dissolved (and most can in petroleum refining), then it will be just as easy to clean the shell side as the tube side. This is an important factor for the process designer to ponder before deciding to place a fluid on the shell or tube side of a heat exchanger.

Fouling Factors

Dirt that sticks to the inside and outside of the tubes interferes with heat transfer. This is called fouling, and the designer should specify the "fouling factors" when he fills out a heat exchanger data sheet. For example:

▶ If the clean heat-transfer coefficient is 100 Btu/hr/ft^2 and a fouling factor of 0.001 is specified on the shell side and 0.001 on the tube-side, the required heat-transfer surface will increase by 20%.

▶ If the clean heat-transfer coefficient is 100 and the total fouling factor specified is 0.010, then required surface area will double.

No one actually knows what fouling factors are in most services, that is, until the exchanger is put on line. One thing is certain: if you specify large fouling factors and purchase an oversized exchanger, you will probably wind up with low fluid velocities and promote fouling. If the process designer really wants to be conservative, a high-velocity, high pressure drop exchanger train should be specified. Naturally, this design philosophy will lead to a greater investment in pumping capacity.

Tube Configuration

Exchanger tubes are usually arranged on a triangular, rotated square or square pitch, with tube spacing (i.e., the distance between the centers of adjacent tubes) of 1 inch, 1¼ inches, and 1½ inches being most common.

In theory, one wishes to minimize tube spacing to increase the number of heat-transfer tubes that can fit into a shell. This certainly reduces the initial cost of a new installation. In practice, one finds that the tubes in a used heat exchanger often look like solidified spaghetti because many of the tubes have sagged against each other. This is a common occurrence in heat exchangers used in hot service. In one case a heat exchanger in crude petroleum service was modified as follows:

Original bundle—1-inch tubes on 1½-inch centers. Square pitch.
New bundle—¾-inch tubes on 1-inch centers. Triangular pitch.

On paper, the heat-transfer surface doubled. In practice, the heat-transfer coefficient rapidly declined after a few months of service until the new bundle was performing below the level of the old square-pitch bundle.

To conclude this chapter, a few rules of thumb are offered:

▶ For condensing clean vapors on the shell side, low fin tubes set on a triangular pitch are excellent.[2]
▶ Boiling fluids on the shell side of an exchanger should employ straight, square-pitch tubes. The idea is to allow vapors to escape from the tube bundle through the space between the tubes.
▶ Using alloy steel tubes rather than plain carbon steel, even when the corrosion environment is not severe, will often be a worthwhile investment. The alloy tubes do not foul as easily as carbon steel and hence will transfer more heat and stay in service longer.

References

1. *Wolverine Trufin Engineering Data Book,* Wolverine Tube Division, Section 2, Second Edition, 1967.
2. TEMA, *The Tubular Exchanger Manufacturers Association Data Book,* Sixth Edition, 1978.

14

Fired Heater Design
for Maximum Run Lengths

I am frequently asked by prospective clients what my principal area of experience is as a process consultant. I always respond that it is the knowledge gained in doing everything wrong the first time. My encounters with fired heaters are a case in point.

My first assignment concerning process heaters was to revamp the delayed coking heater in the Sweet Creek, Kansas Refinery. The name Sweet Creek must have been of ancient Indian origin, because when I saw the creek 20 years ago, it was already an open sewer, flowing more with black oil than water. The delayed coking unit, set on a hill overlooking the befouled creek, was the most important unit in the refinery. It ran well, except for a periodic cleaning of the coking heater tubes. The heater was a typical cabin-type unit shown in Figure 14-1.

Approximately every three months the heater was taken off-line for steam-air decoking of the coils. In this process, coke deposits are burned out of the inside of the coils' tubes using a combination of air and steam. The refinery manager at Sweet Creek had requested the Chicago engineering office to revamp the coking heater to increase its run length to a year. I was given the job of redesigning the heater to accomplish this objective.

The heater shown in Figure 14-1 has two passes, that is, two coils operate in parallel. This was the same configuration as the Sweet Creek Unit, with each of the two coils 1600 feet long. The oil residence time in the coils was 5 minutes, with most of the vaporization occurring in the last 200 feet. As the rate of thermal cracking, and hence coke formation, increases linearly with time, I decided to reduce oil residence time to 2 minutes. This was accomplished by converting the heater from 2 to 4 passes, with each coil 800 feet long.

Oil residence time decreased because the shorter coils reduced pressure drop and vaporization was initiated after just a few hundred feet. Previously,

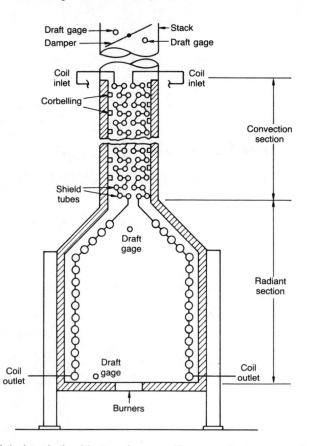

Figure 14-1. A typical cabin-type furnace. (Courtesy *Hydrocarbon Processing.*)

the oil passed through 1400 feet of coil before it began to flash. The earlier vaporization increased the average linear velocity in the tubes, and hence residence time was decreased.

The effect of this modification was startling: heater run lengths decreased from 3 months to 1-2 weeks. This disturbing turn of events was caused by reduced *mass velocities* (also called cold-oil velocity). It is not excessive thermal cracking in a heater's tubes that cause internal coil coking, it is low pressure drop associated with low mass velocity and diminished fluid shear at the tube wall that result in coke deposits.

Mass Velocity

The objective in designing a process heater is to permit maximum firing without overheating the tubes. The principal cause of overheated tubes is localized coke deposits as shown in Figure 14-2. The eventual effect of such coke deposits is that the tube wall will thin out, bulge, and split open (see Figure 14-3). The primary reasons for the formation of coke deposits are excessive heat flux in a localized area, and low fluid wall shear inside the tube.

One of the first lessons a fired heater field engineer learns is that coke deposits are not thickest at the coil outlet where the process fluid is hottest. Usually, the heaviest coke layers are found in the coil at the point just before vaporization is initiated. This is the area of minimum wall shear and maximum fluid temperature.

Vaporization, and the consequent increase in linear velocity and pressure drop, increase the fluid shear forces at the tube wall. But at low mass velocities, field observations indicate that annular flow predominates, rather than a turbulent-type flow. In annular flow, the vapor rushes through the center of the tube, while the liquid creeps along the tube wall. Empirical data suggest that the designer adhere to the guidelines listed in Table 14-1. Incidentally, the Sweet Creek Refinery coking heater had a mass velocity of 60 pounds per square foot per second in the 4 parallel pass configurations.

Velocity Steam

As indicated in Table 14-1, a small amount of steam injected into the coil will reduce coke deposits. The best place to inject this steam is at the inlet of the first tube that is exposed to radiant heat. Not only will the steam create

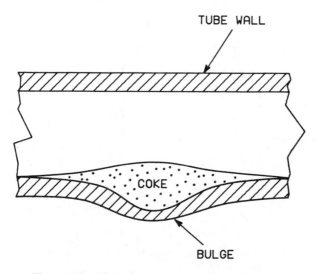

TUBE WALL

COKE

BULGE

Figure 14-2. Coke laydown causes tube thinning.

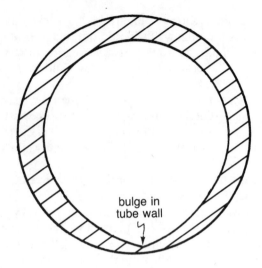

Figure 14-3. Cross section of a heater tube shows the effect of localized overheating.

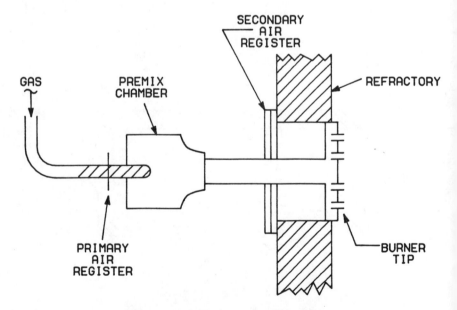

Figure 14-4. Fuel gas premix burner.

Table 14-1
Guidelines for Design of Tube-Size Mass Velocity

Service	Lube Oils Crude Vacuum Hydro Desulfurizer (minimum thermal cracking inside tubes)	Delayed Coker Visbreaker (appreciable thermal cracking inside tubes)
Velocity steam (pounds/barrel)	0-0.5	1.5-2.5
Minimum mass velocity for marginal operation (pounds/ft²/sec.)	40	70
Minimum mass velocity for acceptable operation (pounds/ft²/sec.)	60	120
Recommended design mass velocity for good operation (pounds/ft²/sec.)	120	250

beneficial pressure drop, but it will assist in sweeping the coil clear of liquid in case of a feed interruption. Any loss in feed will result in a temporary low mass velocity and overheated tubes. This type of accident is a leading cause of premature coil coking.

Water injection is an adequate replacement for steam. In many applications water injection is preferred when steam of sufficient pressure is unavailable. Clean steam condensate is best, but I have used water of boiler feedwater quality for years in a visbreaker soaker heater (860°F coil outlet) with no noticeable detrimental effect.

Whether or not steam is used for velocity purposes, emergency steam-out connections are required for each coil. The steam inlets should be valved so that they will open automatically on loss of oil flow to a coil. A manually operated control valve in this service will not provide a fast enough response time.

Heat Flux

Heat flux is measured in Btus per hour per square foot of tube surface (Btu/hr/ft²). The tube surface area is measured on the outside of the tube. When heating liquid hydrocarbons, the following generalizations apply:

▶ 8000 or less heat flux—heater lightly loaded.
▶ 10,000 heat flux—moderate heater load.
▶ 13,000 or more heat flux—heater heavily loaded.

These numbers are *average* heat fluxes, but high average heat fluxes do not often account for ruptured tubes. It is high peak heat flux that causes localized overheating of tubes and failures such as shown in Figure 14-3. Note how the tube is bulged out and the tube wall thinned. This happened because the bottom of the tube was heated to more than 1400°F for several days. If this tube had continued in service, the bulge would have eventually ruptured, hydrocarbons would have sprayed into the firebox, and in the resulting conflagration, the heater could have burned down.

Localized overheating, tube bulging, thinning, and rupture: this is the sequence of events to avoid.

Uneven Heat Distribution

The process engineer cannot leave the design of the heater tube configuration to the manufacturer. Putting blind trust in a vendor is the best way to wind up with inferior process equipment. Items for advance specification to the manufacturer to ensure even heat flux are:

▶ *Tube spacing*—the distance between the tubes in the radiant section must be at least one tube OD (outside diameter). For the last one or two rows of tubes where even heating becomes more critical, a tube spacing of two OD is best. The preceding two rows should be spaced at 1½ OD.
▶ *Tube distance from wall*—placing tubes too close to a wall will keep the back of the tube cooler than the front. This effect can be minimized by placing the tube at least one, and up to two, OD away from the wall. Above two OD, there is no appreciable improvement in heat distribution.
▶ *Maximum primary air*—recall the Bunsen burner in chemistry lab. Remember how a short, dense flame could be obtained by premixing the air and gas in the throat of the burner. It works the same in a process heater. The air premixed with fuel gas is called primary air (see Figure 14-4). The more air that is mixed with the fuel gas, the smaller the flame for a given quantity of heat release. Small, dense flame patterns result in more evenly heated tubes because the source of radiant heat is further from the tubes. The burner manufacturer can maximize primary air when the available fuel-gas pressure is highest. Consider the plant's fuel-gas system, and specify the highest fuel-gas pressure consistantly available.[2]
▶ *Adequate draft*—if insufficient primary air is available to complete combustion of fuel gas, secondary air must be drawn into the firebox. If

there is not at least 5-15% excess air available, yellow flames (i.e., unburnt fuel gas) will wander around the firebox seeking out air to complete combustion. This may result in flame impingement and localized overheating of the tubes. A good design practice to prevent this is to insist that the heater stack height be determined by assuming the stack damper is one-third closed. Also, the secondary air registers should be sized on the basis that they too are one-third closed.

Air Preheater—Effect on Radiant Heat Flux

Preheating combustion air to 400°F will reduce fuel requirements by more than 10%. This is a great way to save energy. But do not forget, especially in the case of retrofits, that preheated air *reduces* the rate of *convective* heat transfer and *increases* the rate of *radiant* heat transfer. After all, if the combustion air is heated by 330°F, the burner adiabatic flame temperature will be about 300°F hotter. If, as a consequence of preheating air, 10% less fuel gas is burnt, the volume of flue gas passing through the convective section is correspondingly reduced and convective heat transfer will be debited by 10%.

Reputable heater manufacturers take the effect of air preheaters into account in their designs. Unfortunately, some vendors of air preheaters for retrofits do not always alert the process design engineer to derate an existing heater limited by firebox temperature when an air preheater is added.

At one time I heard a refinery manager state unequivocally that he could increase the capacity of his crude furnace, which was limited by hot radiant-section tubes, by 10% through addition of an air preheater. After all, he reasoned, 10% less fuel would be required. I pointed out that as the convective section was supplying 30% of the total heat pick up, the reduced flow of flue gas would reduce convective heat recovery by 10%. Consequently, the required heat flux on the radiant tubes would increase by 4%. The refinery manager won the argument. The air preheater was installed and 10% more crude was charged. However, as a result of overfiring, the heater was rendered unfit for service in less than a year. Naturally, in the interim the refinery manager had been promoted to a senior executive position.

Burning Waste Gas

One of the auxiliary functions of a heater is the disposal of low-heating-value waste gas. Combustion of these streams not only saves energy but eliminates a potential environmental problem.

If the waste gas is of too low a pressure to mix with regular fuel gas, it can be charged to a specially designed "wide-range burner," as shown in Figure

14-5. This particular burner can combust gas with a heating value down to 55 Btus per cubic foot. The design of this burner is interesting because air is admitted through the center of the burner, and the gas enters the burner by the outside openings. This is the opposite of a normal burner arrangement.

A forced-air blower is typically required with this burner. Air pressure at the blower discharge should be between 10 inches and 30 inches of water.

Vacuum unit tail gas and asphalt oxidizer vapors are excellent applications for a low-pressure, low-heating-value waste-gas burner.

Convective Section

The flue gas leaving the radiant section is typically between 1200°F and 1500°F. In the convective section the flue gas is cooled to 500-800°F by closely set banks of tubes, as shown in Figure 14-1. The tubes in the convective system usually have extended surfaces—either fins or studs—to improve heat transfer.

Resistance to heat transfer by layers of fouling deposits, just as in a shell-and-tube heat exchanger, are the main problems in the design of convective tubes. Tube-side fouling factors must be specified for heater tubes. The same fouling factors developed for heat-exchange services are suitable for heater convective tubes. For example:

For heavy fouling service	.005 fouling factor
For clean service	.001 fouling factor

Tube-side velocities of less than 3 fps are not a good design practice.

Soot blowers. If oil is to be burned in a heater, provision must be made for soot blowers. Ash, vanadium oxides, and other deposits must be blown from between the fins on the convective tubes. If finned tubes cannot be kept clean, it is better to use bare tubes. A space of 1-2 feet should be left between the rows of convective tubes for soot blowers to be inserted. The soot blowers themselves are just steam lances which can be rotated. A series of holes are cut along the length of the lances.

Finned versus studded tubes. If the fuel to a furnace is low-grade oil with considerable amounts of sediment, vanadium, and salts, the convective tubes should be studded rather than finned. Studded tubes have a large number of spikes contact-welded to their surface. Clearing out deposits between the studs is easier than cleaning finned tubes. A studded tube is also of more rugged construction than a finned tube.

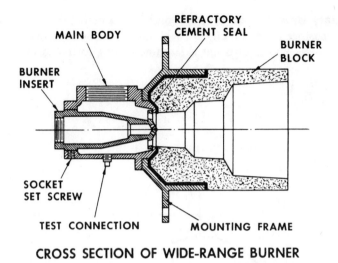

CROSS SECTION OF WIDE-RANGE BURNER

Figure 14-5. Low-pressure, low-Btu-value waste gas can be profitably combusted with a special burner. (Courtesy Maxon Corp.)

Afterburn in convective sections. If the amount of air available in the firebox is not sufficient to complete combustion, the unburnt hydrocarbons enter the convective section. All too frequently, minor leaks in the convective section structure allow air to be drawn into and mixed with the flue gas. After burning then occurs in the midst of the closely set tubes of the convective section. The predictable result is that the fins become an oxidized, fused mass that inhibits rather than promotes heat transfer. To avoid this problem, the designer should provide operating personnel with flue-gas temperature indicators located below, above, and in the middle of the convective section. If the outlet temperature from the convective section is hotter than the inlet, a severe amount of afterburning is occurring. Without such temperature indicators, the operators may wait until they see flames coming out of the heater's stack before cutting back on fuel gas and thus stopping afterburn.

Metallurgy of tubes. High-alloy heater tubes are a good investment for any process plant. Tubes with added strength can withstand occasional overfiring or flame impingement. The chrome content of a tube indicates its resistance to corrosion, especially sulfur. The nickel content improves its strength; most notably nickel raises the temperature at which the tube will start bulging, as shown in Figures 14-2 and 14-3.

Alonized tubes, a process where aluminum is diffused into the surface of tubes, has proved to be a success in services where severe thermal cracking of hydrocarbon feeds are encountered.

Auxiliary drums. Two vessels which are sometimes omitted by the process designer are the fuel-gas knockout drum and the decoking drum. The fuel-gas knockout drum is sized according to the formula

$$V = .5\left(\frac{D_L}{D_V}\right)^{1/2}$$

where:
V = allowable vertical velocity in the drum, fps.

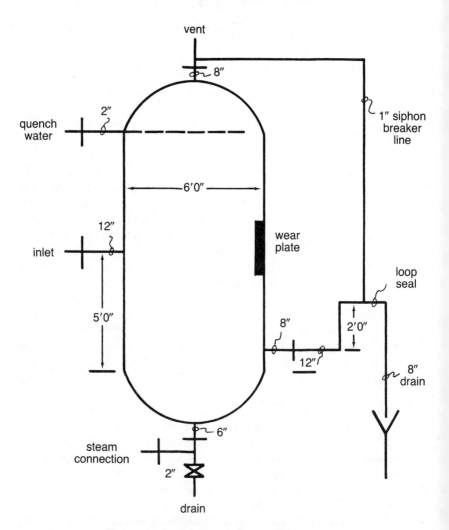

Figure 14-6. A decoking drum for a 6″ coil.

D_L = density of liquid to be separated, usually 40-50 lbs/ft^3.
D_V = density of fuel gas.

The decoking drum is used to cool the effluent gas produced during the steam-air decoking of the heater coils. Figure 14-6 shows the details of one drum used during the decoking of six-inch coils in a visbreaker.

References

1. Goyal, D. P., "Guide Lines Help Combustion Engineers." *Hydrocarbon Processing*, November 1982, p. 205.
2. The Foreman's Page, "Gas-Air Mixture Sets Furnace Efficiency," *The Oil and Gas Journal*, Technical Manual, Part 2.
3. Cratin, R., "Efficient Furnace Firing," Amoco Oil Technical Bulletin, 1976.

15

Corrosion Control Techniques

Most industrial chemicals and hydrocarbon feedstocks are not particularly antagonistic to metals. Concentrated sulfuric acid can easily be stored in carbon steel tanks; aluminum chloride can be dissolved in hot butane and used to catalyize polymerization reactions without damage to steel vessels. The salts in crude oil do no damage to exchangers or tower internals—even at 700°F. However, add water to any one of these systems and steel pipes and vessels can fail in a matter of weeks; sometimes in just a few hours.

The designer can avoid creating many corrosive environments by following a few simple rules concerning the presence of water in process units:

▶ Avoid the condensation of steam to water.
▶ Do not allow pockets of water to accumulate inside process vessels or in dead-ended piping.
▶ Neutralize low-pH condensate as quickly as possible.

Controlling Condensate pH in Crude Oil Distillation

When crude oil containing salt is heated over 350°F, the salt decomposes to hydrochloric acid which condenses along with water in the crude unit overhead system. This condensation can cause severe corrosion. Actually, it is only the magnesium and calcium chloride salts that decompose. Sodium chloride, which represents about 90% of the total salt content, is heat stable and drops into the bottoms product.

The problem is best solved by complete desalting of the crude oil. But desalting is not always possible, especially with heavy viscous crudes. Every effort should be made to reduce the salt content of the desalted crude to less than 5 pounds of salt per 1000 barrels of crude. Figure 15-1 shows a single-stage desalter.

The first corrective measure is the injection of caustic soda into the desalted crude to neutralize the hydrochloric acid as soon as it is liberated in the heat exchangers and heater. This method, while cheap and simple, is not always completely effective, and the injection rate is limited to meet asphalt specifications and avoid fouling and coking of downstream heaters and exchangers. A maximum rate of 3 pounds of NaOH per 1000 barrels is typical.

The hydrochloric acid which is not neutralized by the caustic injection may be neutralized with ammonia injected into the fractionator or into the overhead line. If there is free water on the fractionator trays, which is very undesirable, injection into the tower itself can result in ammonium chloride deposits and tower plugging.

The formation of free water inside a tower can be avoided by maintaining the tower top temperature 10-15°F above the calculated dew point of water. This dew point is calculated as follows:

1. $PP_w = \left(\dfrac{M_w}{M_w + M_{HC}}\right) \times (P_t)$

where:
PP_w = partial pressure water.
M_w = moles of water in tower overhead.
M_{HC} = moles of net overhead product plus reflux.
P_t = total pressure.

2. From a steam table, determine the steam saturation temperature that corresponds to PP_w.

The tower top temperature should be maintained 10-15°F above that calculated in step 2. Incidentally, do not forget to include the water dissolved in the tower top reflux when calculating M_w.

The safest injection point for ammonia is into the vapor line as close as possible to the top of the tower. The ammonia injection rate should be controlled by two parallel rotameters: one for normal operation, and one for use in the event of desalter failure. Copper alloys must *not* be used anywhere in the overhead system, since ammonia attacks copper. Those crude units with admiralty tube bundles in the overhead system must not use ammonia, as an excess of ammonia will cause rapid destruction of the bundles.

Since there are other corrosive agents in addition to hydrochloric acid, it is frequently desirable to inject a proprietary oil-soluble corrosion inhibitor into the overhead system. The effectiveness of any corrosion inhibitor is

TYPICAL LOW VELOCITY DESALTER

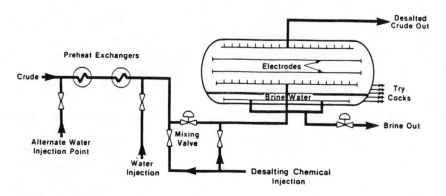

Figure 15-1. Extracting chloride salts before they thermally decompose to HCl will prevent corrosion.

greatly increased and the dosage and cost reduced if the inhibitor is dissolved in a 5-10-gpm slip stream of reflux liquid and then dispersed into the overhead vapor through a high-velocity sparger located in the vapor line close to the top of the tower.

Most overhead corrosion takes place in the areas where water, with hydrochloric acid, is condensing. The condensate should be neutralized by flooding that area with neutral wash water. This is done by recirculating wash water from the overhead receiver, as shown in Figure 15-2.

The recirculated wash water should be injected into the overhead system just before the point at which water condensation starts. Depending on the design, this can be before or after the overhead/crude exchangers. Where there are parallel condensing trains, the water must be uniformly distributed through spargers with adequate pressure drop. Water injection reduces the differential temperature across the condenser, and a loss in heat transfer results.

Equipment Sizing

The caustic injection pump should be sized for 100 gallons per day for each 10,000 BSD of crude charge. A single-plunger chemical injection-type pump with a continuously variable rate should be specified.

The caustic should be diluted to 2-3 weight percent of NaOH. A Monel quill, extending one-third of the way into the pipe diameter, should be used. The injection point should be immediately downstream of the desalter at a process temperature of not more than 300°F.

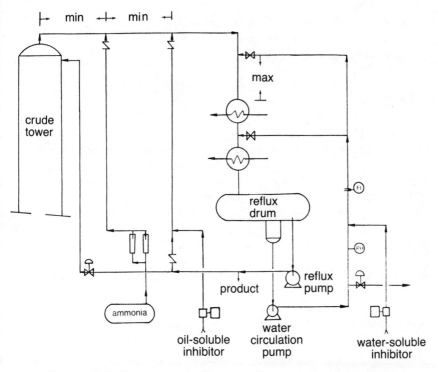

Figure 15-2. Corrosion control in a crude unit overhead system.

Ammonia is usually pressured out of storage cylinders, and no injection pumps are required. The required rate can be calculated by the amount of hydrogen chloride liberated when the magnesium chloride and calcium chloride salts decompose. When these data are not available, the rate of ammonia usage can be assumed at 15-100 pounds per day per 10,000 BSD crude.

The oil-soluble chemical injection pump is the same type as that specified for the caustic injection pump. The pump is sized for 10-20 gallons per day for each 10,000 BSD of overhead product plus reflux.

In practice, I have found that undersizing the water circulation pump shown in Figure 15-2 is a most common mistake. This pump should be sized for a water recirculation rate of 10% of the total hydrocarbon overhead product plus reflux, in addition to handling the normal net overhead water. Do not forget to allow 15-25 psi extra discharge pressure for the vapor line internal-water sparger. The sparger itself should be a ¾ of an inch pipe with the number of holes set according to

$$H_s = \frac{W_R}{70 \, D^2}$$

where:

H_s = number of holes in sparger.

W_R = wash-water rate, gpm.

D = hole diameter, inches.

Dead Ends

Any place that water can stagnate is a candidate for corrosion and mechanical failure. Corrosive salts may concentrate in these pockets.

Dead spaces in heat exchangers can be avoided by the strategic location of baffles. Seldom-used piping and control valves can be elevated so that they will be self-draining. The draw-off nozzles on vessels should be designed flush with collection pans or the bottom head. It is not sufficient to specify a low-point bleeder in the expectation that operating personnel will periodically drain off the accumulated water.

Water Accumulation Can Cause Hydrogen Blistering of Steel

It is possible for atomic hydrogen to diffuse through the crystal lattice of iron and form pockets of molecular hydrogen inside the metal walls of a vessel. This process is called hydrogen blistering and in severe cases can lead to failure of the vessel wall.

Cyanides are formed in appreciable concentrations, especially in refinery fluid-cracking units (FCU). In the presence of free water and hydrogen sulfide, cyanides react with the iron sulfide on the vessel walls to produce atomic hydrogen, which can diffuse into the vessel wall. These elements are all present in an FCU gas absorber.

To minimize the effects of hydrogen blistering, wash water (usually of boiler feedwater quality) is brought into contact with the FCU overhead vapors. The absorber liquid feed drum is designed conservatively for a good water-hydrocarbon liquid separation. In a horizontal separator the superficial vertical velocity of the hydrocarbon should be not more than 25 feet per hour. This will allow sufficient time for the droplets of water to settle out.

Most important, water which accumulates on the trays inside the absorber must be removed. Inspection of FCU absorbers clearly shows the most severe hydrogen blistering attack two or three trays below the unstabilized liquid feed nozzle. This is because the temperature profile and pressure of the absorber prevent water from leaving the bottom of the tower as a liquid or the top of the tower as a vapor in quantities equal to the water in the feed. To prevent the resulting accumulation of water, a trap-out tray is necessary.

Figure 15-3 illustrates a typical water trap-out tray. The trap-out pan is too small to make a decent separation between water and hydrocarbon. A mixed phase is drawn-off and flows to a small drum (boot) located at grade. The

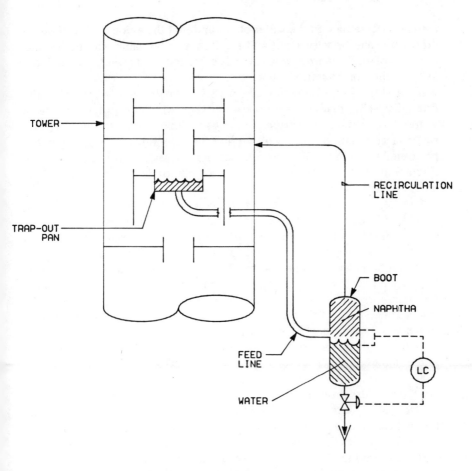

Figure 15-3. Removing water trapped inside a distillation tower.

boot is sized for 10-15 minutes residence time. Hold time in the trap-out pan can be as little as 15 seconds.

In the boot a good separation is made between the two phases. Water is drawn-off; the hydrocarbon flows back to the absorber through the recirculation line. The driving force for producing the flow of liquid through the boot is the density difference between the liquid in the feed line and the recirculation line.

Draining Small Amounts of Water Continuously

Corrosion due to free water in distillation columns is a common and serious problem. Proper designs must recognize that particulate matter tends to accumulate in the water phase and that the amount of water to be drawn off may be very small and the flow very variable. In one instance internals of a debutanizer were severely damaged due to water accumulating in the debutanizer reflux drum.

Inevitably, a small amount of corrosion particles settled in the reflux drum. These particles plugged the water draw-off control valve so that the water level in the reflux drum could not be held automatically. Since the water accumulation rate was variable, a program to have operating personnel drain the water manually was not successful. Water in the reflux drum built up to the level of the reflux draw-off nozzle and was then refluxed back down the tower.

The free water (saturated with hydrogen sulfide) was heated to 400°F in the 200-psig debutanizer. In a matter of months this new tower suffered severe damage. The 7% chrome reboiler bundle developed dozens of tube leaks and had to be retubed. The stainless-steel valve trays were corroded to the point that tray efficiency was impaired. Bottom tray leakage became so high that liquid flow to the thermosyphon reboiler was lost. The debutanizer bottoms product became contaminated with large amounts of particulate iron sulfide. The entire tower had to be retrayed. Cumulative production losses were more than $1 million.

What initiated this problem, and how could it have been prevented? The fundamental cause was designing the water draw-off control valve to handle very small volumes of water. Also, the control valve was designed to take a 180-psi pressure drop. These factors led to an extremely small port size in the control valve. Corrosion particles from the debutanizer reflux drum settled out in the boot and plugged the control valve's small port. During periods of low water flow to the reflux drum, the control valve tended to clog up with corrosion products. Operator intervention to drain the boot manually was not consistent enough to prevent the frequent refluxing of water back to the tower.

To correct this problem, the facilities shown in Figure 15-4 were installed. The water draw-off control valve intervals were changed to provide a larger port opening. To keep the control valve and associated piping from clogging during periods of low water flow from the reflux drum, an external source of water was pumped into the outlet line from the boot. This kept the control valve operating in a fairly open position. The source of this "flushing" water was the sour water tank. Therefore, no incremental sour water was generated.

Carbon Dioxide in Steam Is Corrosive

One of the most frequent maintenance jobs on a process unit is plugging leaking tubes in steam reboilers. Often, the tube leaks are caused by

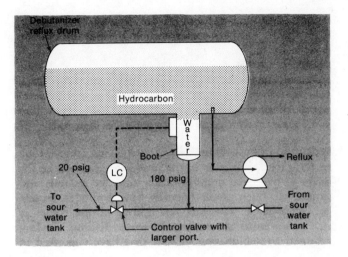

Figure 15-4. Preferred design to prevent water draw-off control valve plugging. (Courtesy *Hydrocarbon Processing.*)

corrosion on the steam side. Trace quantities of CO_2 in the steam (which is normally on the tube side of a shell-and-tube reboiler) accumulate at the top of the channel head and floating head. Figure 15-5 illustrates the problem.

Accumulated CO_2 must be vented off to prevent excessive tube corrosion. Venting CO_2 from the top of the channel head is a simple and common practice. Venting the floating-head end (assuming the reboiler is the usual "pull-through, floating-head" type) is rarely done. However, failure to vent the floating end has resulted in tube leaks near the floating head. A novel method to accomplish this function is depicted in Figure 15-5.

A one-inch pipe is welded onto the channel side tube sheet adjoining the tube to be used as a "vent tube." Another one-inch pipe is welded into the channel head itself. When the exchanger is assembled, the channel-head cover is left off the channel head. The one-inch pipes on the channel head and the tube sheet are coupled up by a worker from inside the channel head. The channel-head cover is now attached. The floating-head end can then be vented as required.

Use Corrosion to Prevent Corrosion

The best way to fight fire is with fire. Similarly, corrosive action can be used to advantage to stop destructive corrosion. There are two examples of this technique:

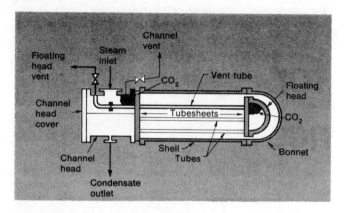

Figure 15-5. Conventional pull-through, floating-head, shell and tube re-boiler showing accumulation of corrosive CO_2.

▶ Many corrosive systems produce a protective layer of corrosion products which adhere to metal walls. If low fluid velocities are maintained, this protective layer is left intact and will then stop further corrosion.

▶ The fundamental electrical nature of corrosion can be used to protect process equipment by utilizing the different galvanic potentials of metals.

Sacrificial Anode

When dissimilar metals are in contact in the presence of an electrolyte (such as salt or cooling tower water) the more anodic of the two metals is rapidly attacked, while the rate of corrosion to the more cathodic metal is retarded. In process equipment this type of association of dissimilar metals is most often encountered in shell-and-tube heat exchangers. For example, a condenser is fabricated with admirality brass tubes and steel-tube support baffles.

This type of deterioration is called galvanic corrosion. It is favored by highly conductive electrolytes (i.e., using acid-contaminated water in an exchanger is a lot more conducive to galvanic attack than employing distilled water as a coolant). Also, closely coupling metals with large potential galvanic differences also accelerates corrosion. Table 15-1 lists commercially employed metals in order of their tendency to corrode galvanically with the more anodic (less noble) metals at the top.

This phenomenon can be used to advantage when sacrificial anodes are used to increase the life of expensive cathodic exchanger parts. For example, in water coolers where copper-alloy tubes are used with steel-tube sheets, a zinc sacrificial anode is installed. This anode corrodes, and in so doing protects the more anodic steel-tube sheet. When filling out an exchanger data sheet, the process designer who specifies materials of construction should also make a notation that a sacrificial anode is required whenever dissimilar metals are used in the presence of salt or acid containing water.

Excessive Velocity Erosion

Many metal surfaces form their own protective coating consisting of a thin layer of corrosion products. Once in place, this protective film stops further corrosion. Instances of metal failure attributed to erosion are often really due to corrosion in the sense that erosive forces have wiped away the protective layer of corrosion products and exposed the clean metal surface to further corrosion.

To reduce this erosive-corrosive action, velocities of liquids in process equipment and piping should be kept at less than 12 fps. This is also a good criterion for mixed-phase (vapor and liquid) streams which have at least 50 weight percent of liquid.

For liquids which carry an appreciable load of solids, erosive reduction of the protective film is accelerated. A maximum velocity of 8-10 fps is normal for such systems. However, do not permit velocities to fall below 3-5 fps so that precipitation of the solids is prevented.

Table 15-1
Galvanic Series of Metals and Alloys in Seawater

MOST ANODIC
Magnesium
Zinc
Aluminum
Mild steel
Wrought iron
Cast iron
410 S.S.—active
316 S.S.—active
Admiralty brass
Copper
Aluminum bronze
Nickel
Inconel
410 S.S.—passive
316 S.S.—passive
Monel
Hastelloy C
Titanium
MOST CATHODIC

Areas of fluid impingement and high turbulence are exposed to excessive rates of corrosion-erosion. Piping on the outlets of condensers is most susceptible to accelerated corrosion. On a unit I supervised in Texas City, this fact was dramatically demonstrated.

The incident occurred on an alkylation unit refrigerant depropanizer. One morning, the first elbow on the reflux drum outlet liquid line ruptured. Hundreds of barrels of propane and isobutane spilled out. The resulting cloud of hydrocarbon vapors detonated when it reached a fired heater. After the fires subsided, I inspected the elbow and found a section of piping the size of a sardine can lid had been peeled back. The metal was literally paper thin. Curiously, the area of failure was on the inside of the elbow.

To prevent such incidents, low velocity and long radius bends should be specified by the process designer for the outlet of any surface condenser in light hydrocarbon service.

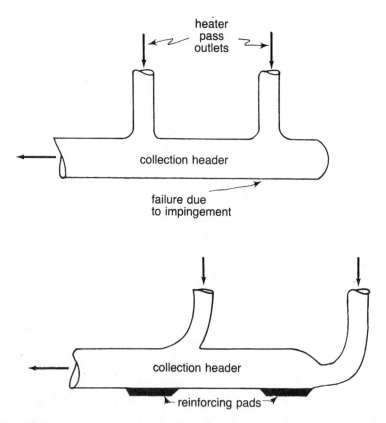

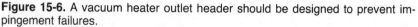

Figure 15-6. A vacuum heater outlet header should be designed to prevent impingement failures.

Taking care of such details may properly seem to be the job of the mechanical designer, rather than the process engineer. This assumption is incorrect because the mechanical designer is unlikely to be cognizant of peculiar process conditions which can lead to rapid metal deterioration.

Another common example of piping failure resulting from impingement occurs at the outlets of vacuum heaters. Figure 15-6 illustrates both the wrong and right ways to tie individual pass outlets into a collection header. I have been involved in two fires resulting from this particular kind of impingement failure. A notation made on the original process flowsheet stating "Pass Outlets to Be Piped into Header with Long Radius Elbows" could have prevented these fires.

References

1. McDonald, G. W., The IONA Company, New Jersey, "Crude Unit Corrosion Control," private communication to N. Lieberman 6/8/82.

2. UOP Process Division, "Corrosion & Fouling Management," 3/82.

3. Lieberman, N., "Design Processes for Reduced Maintenance," *Hydrocarbon Processing,* January 1979, p. 92.

16

Safety

"Safety in the process industry does not start with the man who operates the equipment. It starts with the process designer. It should not be necessary for each generation to rediscover principles of process safety which the generation before discovered. We must learn from the experience of others rather than the hard way."[1]

These words were written by J. Ducommun, a former oil industry executive. They were based on a number of tragic accidents which, with proper process design, might have been avoided. Certainly, the process design engineer can have a decisive influence on the fundamental safety of an operating plant.

Safety on a process unit in the context of this chapter refers to preventing equipment damage or failure during abnormal operations, such as:

▶ Start-ups.
▶ Shutdowns.
▶ Sudden changes in feed quality or rate.
▶ Loss of electric power.
▶ Loss of other utilities such as steam, cooling water, instrument air, or boiler feedwater.
▶ Liquid level control malfunctions.

Start-Ups and Shutdowns

The critical times during a flight are when the airplane takes off and lands. The history of process plant operations teaches the same lesson: start-ups and shutdowns are the most dangerous periods.

There are two general sources of hazards which must be avoided: (1) rapid flashing of water to steam, and (2) mixing air and combustibles inside process vessels.

The first step in putting a piece of process equipment in service is air freeing. This is accomplished by purging with steam or nitrogen, or less commonly, filling with water. Steam is usually a cheaper and quicker medium for purging than nitrogen. However, if the plant is designed for refrigeration service, the external insulation may not be able to withstand the 250-300°F metal temperatures caused by steam purging. Also, some reactors with acid-based catalyst or vessels with KOH pellets can be degraded by moisture. In such cases a nitrogen purge is necessary.

To size purge lines, the following criteria should be used:

▶ Calculate volume of equipment to be purged.
▶ Multiply volume by four.
▶ Assume a 10-hour purge period.

Successful purging requires that there be no high-point pockets in process vessels. To avoid the necessity of installing a high-point vent on top of a vessel, the normal process outlet nozzle should be located on top of the vessel. As these high-point vents are often difficult to climb up to, the operators frequently forget to close them. On one distillation column, this omission cost 10% of the propylene overhead product production for a week before the vent valve was closed.

Purge lines—either steam or nitrogen—should not be designed to be permanently connected to a high-pressure process vessel. A piping spool piece should be removed from the purge line after the plant is on-line. This is required to prevent high-pressure hydrocarbons from backing into the purge system. On one unit, 300-psig propane leaked past a steam purge connection into a 150-psig steam system. The problem was finally discovered when an operator observed propane vapors, instead of steam, being emitted from a fire-suppressant steam-purge nozzle.

Hazards of Water

Unplanned or accidental introduction of water into hot-oil systems usually results in tremendous overloads on equipment—overloads that equipment cannot be designed to withstand. Explosions and fires following such accidents have cost many lives and resulted in tremendous equipment damage.[2]

In my career I have witnessed many incidents where process vessels were damaged by water suddenly flashing to steam. In comparison, I only recall two accidents involving equipment failure due to accidental air introduction in vessels. Water, which has a molecular weight of 18, will occupy about 10 times the volume, when vaporized, as a gallon of hydrocarbon boiling at the same temperature as water. Therefore, the potential to generate large volumes of vapor is much greater with water than with hydrocarbons. In practice, as long as the heaviest component being vaporized overhead has a normal boiling point of 200°F or less, the explosive flashing of water is not frequently a problem. It is when process equipment is designed to boil off liquids with a normal boiling point of 500-1000°F, that one encounters the overwhelming force of flashing water.

The most common example of this problem is the upsetting of distillation tower trays in a fractionating column. The chances of an inexperienced or inattentive operating crew blowing out the trays of a crude column on start-up with water are about 9 chances in 10. The surest way to cause such an accident is to heat the bottom of the crude column to 700°F *before* circulating through the bottom pumparound circuit. Next, turn on the circulating pumparound pump without draining the lines. The water thus pumped back to the crude column is guaranteed to wreck the trays.

How can the process designer assist the operators in avoiding such incidents? First, provide adequate drain holes on all column internals. This is not to say that every section of tray, trap-out, and downcomer seal pan must have a drain hole. On the contrary, excessive use of drain holes ruins fractionation due to excessive internal leakage.

All fractionation trays, with the exception of bubble-cap decks, are self-draining. The seal pan shown in Figure 16-1 requires a drain hole. The draw-off pan will not need a drain hole if the draw-off nozzle is built flush with the bottom of the pan.

A drain hole needs to be large enough to reduce the chances of it plugging, and small enough to minimize internal leakage during normal operation. For clean, noncorrosive services I have used a one-quarter inch hole; while for black oil, potential corrosive services I have specified a three-quarters inch hole. A single hole is sufficient for nonself-draining flat surfaces of up to 50 square feet.

Avoid undrainable dead spaces adjacent to or inside vessels that cannot be circulated. The lower the start-up pressure of a tower, the more damaging relatively small quantities of flashing water can be. Even just a few gallons of trapped water, which have been suddenly exposed to 500°F oil, are sufficient to upset the trays in a large vacuum still.[3]

Dehydrating by Circulation

It is not possible to water-free process equipment simply by draining. Even if a distillation column is pressured to 100 psig with dry inert gas, and every low-point drain is blown dry, the column will still contain water. The

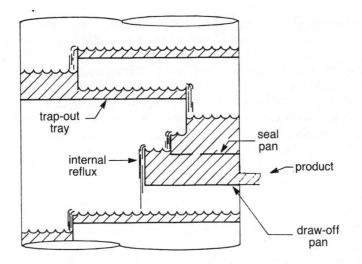

Figure 16-1. To prevent potentially damaging accumulations of water in a distillation tower, a drain hole is required in the seal pan.

only positive method to water-free process equipment is oil circulation followed by repeated draining of low points.

It is the process designer's job to review the plant's P & IDs (process and instrumentation drawings) to ensure that sufficient low-point drains are provided on piping, control valve loops, heat exchangers, pumps, drums and vessels. Remember that every small connection is a potential point of mechanical failure. Therefore, provide only the necessary drain connection.

The P & IDs must also be reviewed for start-up lines. For example, it will be necessary to circulate oil through the pumparound circuits and across the trays of a crude oil tower to flush out water. The normal way that oil reaches the upper trays and pumparound draw-offs is through vaporization of the feed. But the purpose of dehydration is to water-free the equipment before hot oil is introduced, and vaporization cannot take place before heating the oil feed. To overcome this quandry, a start-up line is required. This line will deliver a clean oil stream to the upper part of the crude column. The return line of the uppermost pumparound is the ideal place to connect the start-up oil.

Size the start-up oil line for approximately 20% of the net distillate product rate. The oil introduced into the tower will flow into all the pumparound and product drawoff pumps. Circulation can then be established in the lower pumparound circuits. Operations personnel will periodically stop the circulation, allow water to settle out, and drain the low points before restarting the pumparound pumps.

Areas inside the tower that cannot be reached by flushing oil should be eliminated from the design. A drain hole is not sufficient protection from water accumulations, as the hole can plug. Nonessential connections to the pumparound circuits should be avoided. During routine operations, long after a crude column has been started, an operator may decide to open a valve on some seldom used jumpover line. All too often, such lines have not been made water-free during start-up. The few gallons of water that can return to the hot tower from the previously idle line can easily upset the trays in the crude tower.

Fluctuating Feed

No one can be expected to design a unit to guard against every contingency. But a piece of equipment that self-destructs due to a sudden loss in feed has certainly not been properly designed. For example, a fired heater can be severely damaged when the pump charging liquid to its coils shuts down. It is not sufficient to instantly stop fuel flow to the burners whenever the feed is interrupted. The hot internal refractory contains enough heat to damage the heater's tubes for several minutes after firing is discontinued. Steam must be introduced into the coils as soon as liquid flow is lost to prevent the tubes' metal walls from overheating and sagging. The instantaneous response required can only be effected by a low liquid flow trip automatically triggering steam flow.

Any process which is exothermic has an inherent safety problem. Reaction rates always increase at higher temperature. If the higher rate of reaction liberates more heat, the process can proceed with explosive force.

Hydrocracking reactions are a good example of a potentially dangerous exothermic reaction. I well remember one giant unit, owned by Exxon in New Jersey, whose explosive demise affected the whole petroleum industry. In this unit petroleum resid was hydrocracked to lighter productions under a 2000-psig hydrogen pressure and a temperature of 800°F. Heat was removed from the reactor by introducing cool hydrogen and liquid feed and withdrawing hot products.

The problem in such a reactor is what to do if the reaction gets out of hand, as for instance, when the cool liquid feed is stopped. The loss of the cool liquid immediately raises the reactor temperature. This accelerates the rate of the hydrocracking reaction, which releases more heat.

As this particular reactor was full of liquid, there was certainly plenty of fuel to continue the reaction. The superficial response to curtail the reaction and heat release would be to stop the hydrogen flow. Unfortunately, the short-term effects of interrupting the flow of cool hydrogen to the reactor would further raise the reactor internal temperature.

There are two possible solutions to this common problem:

▶ *The design of the reactor should be based on limiting the inventory of reactants.* This limit is based on the reaction going to completion without overheating—or overpressuring—the reactor. This can be a rather complex problem. For instance, even after all the hydrogen is consumed in a hydrocracker, further heat-generating reactions, such as polymerization, can still take place.

▶ *Impede the rate of reaction.* In a hydrocracker this can best be done by including in the design a provision to depressure the reactor rapidly. As the rate of hydrocracking is directly related to hydrogen partial pressure, venting off the hydrogen materially slows the reaction.

Of course, as in everything in life, one can overdo the safety aspects of process design. The case of a wax hydrotreating unit I designed comes to mind. This unit purified yellow wax by bringing the wax into contact with 2200-psig hydrogen inside a fixed-bed vertical reactor, such as is shown in Figure 16-2. One day the flow of cool-quench hydrogen between the beds was inadvertently cut off. The reactor rapidly began to overheat. Foresightedly, I had anticipated this contingency and designed a large vent at the top of the reactor. When opened, this vent would rapidly depressure the wax hydrotreater and stop the reaction dead in its tracks.

When the operators went to use this vent, something quite unforeseen transpired. The rapidly upflowing vapors created a large upward pressure gradiant. As the reactor internals had been designed for downflow, the catalyst bed supports were designed to withstand only a downward force. Hence, opening up the large emergency vent violently lifted the catalyst and bed supports against the top of the reactor. When the reactor was opened, the inspector was greeted by a sight of great havoc.

A properly designed vent should have been located on the bottom of the reactor. Also, it should have been limited in size so that when opened completely, a reasonable pressure drop would have resulted.

Water in Feed

A slug of water charged to a hot-oil distillation column will flash to steam with explosive force. To prevent the inevitable tray damage, the process designer must rigorously exclude the possibility of water entering a hot process vessel.

A simple, practical method of dealing with this problem is to utilize a conductivity cell. This device can differentiate between water and oil based on the much greater electrical conductivity of water versus oil. A sudden increase in the conductivity of the feed generates a signal to trip off the feed pump.

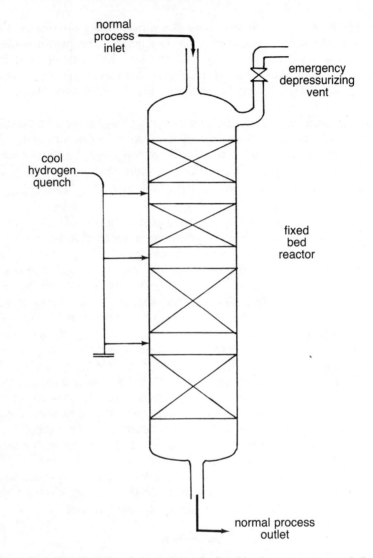

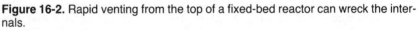

Figure 16-2. Rapid venting from the top of a fixed-bed reactor can wreck the internals.

In practice, I have found that permitting a slug of water to enter a process heater does not damage downstream equipment. The immense backpressure generated by the water as it flashes in the heater coils will usually cause the charge pump to bog down.

Electric Power Failure

Of all the utilities serving a process plant, electricity is the least reliable. The designer must always consider how the plant can be safely shut down during a complete power failure. A few tips are:

▶ Critical pumps required to pump out the unit during shutdown should be *spared* (i.e., duplicate pump provided on stand-by) with a steam turbine-driven pump.
▶ A small steam turbine-driven electric power generator should be included in the design to provide lights and power to the control room.
▶ For heavy-oil service, a diesel-driven flushing oil pump is necessary to prevent the oil from solidifying in process piping during a combined steam and power failure.

Loss of Cooling

When a total power failure occurs, electric-driven cooling-water pumps and air-cooled fin-fans stop. Heat removal from the process is quickly curtailed. However, heat input from fired heaters and steam reboilers will continue for a while, even after operators have blocked in the steam and fuel gas valves.

It helps to design the fuel-gas control valves to shutdown automatically on power failure. A more positive method is to have one-quarter of the cooling-water supply pumps powered by a steam drive. The louvers on fin-fan coolers can be designed to open on electric power failure.

Instrument Air Failure

For a plant with pneumatically operated instruments and controls, loss of instrument air pressure is a serious and, all too often, common occurrence. The process designer must designate, for each control valve, whether it will open or close when air pressure is lost to its diaphragm. The objective is to ensure that the plant will not self-destruct due to an instrument air failure. A few examples will clarify this point:

▶ *Fuel-gas control valve*—should close on loss of air pressure (this is called "air failure closes" or AFC). If the control valve was to air-fail open (AFO), fuel gas would flow uncontrollably to the heater's burners and perhaps burn the furnace down.
▶ *Condenser cooling-water control valve*—should AFO (open on loss of air pressure). If the valve was to AFC (close on loss of air pressure), the loss of cooling would cause the condenser to overpressure.

The designer has to think through each situation individually and carefully consider the interrelationship between equipment before deciding if a control valve is to AFO or AFC.

In one refinery the potential for plant-wide instrument air failures was eliminated by connecting the inert gas system (nitrogen) to the instrument air system, as shown in Figure 16-3. Note how the motive gas for the control valve connecting nitrogen to the instrument air header is supplied from the nitrogen header. *CAUTION:* the nitrogen will also flow into board-mounted controllers and displace the air in control rooms. Hence, adequate ventilation must be provided in the control room whenever the nitrogen backup control valve opens into the instrument air system.

Level Control

The difficulty of measuring levels has led to many disasters in process plants. Level control can be no better than level measurement, and a separate chapter is devoted to this subject. The following incident, which occurred in Texas City, will suffice to illustrate the problem.

Gasoline was circulated through a high-pressure absorber to recover propane before the off-gas was vented to the refinery fuel-gas system. One evening, the level indication on the absorber was lost. The 150-foot tower filled with liquid, which spilled over into the overhead knockout drum. This vessel, along with the downstream refinery fuel-gas collection drum, also overflowed with gasoline. Eventually, the liquid reached the dozen or so fired heater fuel-gas knockout drums scattered through the refinery. These too overflowed. Gasoline spilled out of the burners and fires erupted underneath many of the heaters.

The key to avoiding such safety hazards lies in redundant liquid level indication, where two level-sensing devices are completely independent. If one liquid level indicator is only 90% reliable, then two indicators are 99%

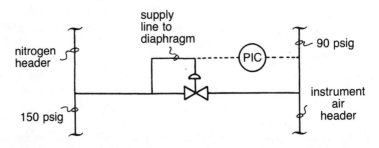

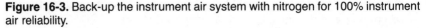

Figure 16-3. Back-up the instrument air system with nitrogen for 100% instrument air reliability.

reliable. Design details for liquid level indication are discussed in the following chapter.

Anticipating Heat Exchanger Leaks

Shell-and-tube heat exchangers are the most numerous type of process equipment in a plant. The tubes in the exchanger have about ⅟₁₆-inch thick walls. Relatively small amounts of corrosion or mechanical stress will initiate failure in these thin-wall tubes. Sooner or later, the process designer must anticipate that all exchangers will leak. If the shell side is at higher pressure than the tube side, then shell-side fluid will leak into the tube-side fluid. Naturally, the converse is also true.

Considerations of the safety consequences of tube leaks can have a decisive influence on the process flow. Figure 16-4 is a simple example of the problem.

A 600°F asphalt stream was produced from the bottom of a vacuum distillation unit. Before the asphalt could be rundown to tankage, it had to be cooled to 400°F. The proposed design was to cool the asphalt by generating 150-psig steam. In this case the tube side of the heat exchanger would have operated at 10 psig, while the shell side would be under a 150-psig water pressure.

Now suppose a tube is ruptured in the steam generator. Water would be pressured into the tube side. Initially, the water would simply flash to steam on the oil side. However, after a few minutes, the large volume of steam would backout the asphalt flowing into the exchanger. Then, water would

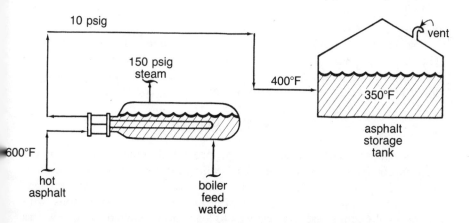

Figure 16-4. A tube leak in the steam generator can blow the roof off the asphalt tank.

flow down the asphalt line to the asphalt tank. When the water mixed with the 350°F asphalt, it would violently flash to steam. The atmospheric vent on the tank could never handle the huge volume of steam thus generated, and a pressure of several psig would develop inside the tank. As cone roof tanks are not intended or designed for pressure service, the roof would be blown off.

Incidents similar to this one have happened. To avoid such an occurrence, the asphalt must be cooled with a circulating oil stream or used to preheat crude oil. If a tube leak then develops, the cool oil flowing into the asphalt tank will contaminate the asphalt product, but no safety problems will develop.

Vessel Collapse

One of the most frightening refinery experiences I have had is to watch the exterior of a 10-foot diameter drum being sucked in by internal vacuum. The incident occurred when a steam condensate collection drum half full of hot water was rapidly cooled.

Hot water from throughout the refinery was collected in the drum. As the combined temperature of the water was 220°F, the drum, which was vented to the atmosphere, normally ran under a slight positive pressure. A 2-inch vent line allowed a small amount of flashed steam to escaped from the drum.

On this particular occasion, the flow of condensate was interrupted. As a consequence, the water level in the drum dropped precipitately. The operator on duty noted the falling water level and immediately opened a large valve to refill the drum with 80°F water. The cold water rapidly condensed the steam, and a vacuum was created inside the vessel. Air was sucked in through the 2-inch vent, but not fast enough to prevent the collapse of the vessel.

This accident could have been avoided by designing a large enough vent. The maximum volume of steam that can be condensed can easily be calculated based on the flow rate of the cold water. The vent is then sized to admit sufficient air into the drum to replace the condensed steam.

A Word of Caution

This chapter can, at best, alert the process designer to a few of the uncountable types of safety problems which must be considered in plant design. The American Petroleum Institute (API) has put out an excellent series on this subject. Field observations and frank discussions with operating personnel are the best way to learn how to avoid unsafe process design practices. A few extra hours of thought may someday save lives and millions of dollars.

References

1. Engineering for Safe Operations, "The American Oil Company," 1966.
2. American Petroleum Institute, "Safety Digest of Lessons Learned," Section Two, *Safety in Unit Operations,* 1979.
3. "Hazard of Water in Refinery Process Systems," Standard Oil Company, Indiana Fourth Edition, 1960.
4. American Petroleum Institute "Safety Digest of Lessons Learned," Section Three, *Safe Operations of Auxiliaries,* 1980.

17

Liquid Level Control

The reflection of the flare shimmered in Galveston Bay as I drove across the Causeway. Both the night sky above the refinery and the black waters of the bay were illuminated by the glowing flare. From a distance of 10 miles I could tell that something was wrong in the plant.

My boss, Mr. Overborne, had awakened me at 1:00 a.m. He stated that things were amiss in the refinery and suggested that I drive out to the plant to investigate. So at 2:00 a.m. I pulled up to the control room.

I sat in the car a few minutes, trying to suppress my excitement and irritation before confronting the operating crew. The refinery was bathed in the yellow light from the flare. "A rather expensive way to light up the plant," I remember thinking. "Burning 5000 BSD of propane and butane."

Bobby was sitting in front of the instrument board when I entered the control room. The other operators were huddled around the chief's desk.

Starting quietly, I ventured, "What's going on Bobby?"

"Oh, nothing much, Mr. Lieberman, everything's pretty routine tonight."

"It looks like something is going to the flare though, Bobby. Any idea where it's coming from?"

Bobby looked up at the miniature sun, blazing in the night sky, its intensity barely diminished by the dirty control room window. "It looks like we might be venting a little propane vapor from the depropanizer reflux drum. I've been getting a low liquid level in the drum all night. Johnson opened the vapor vent from the top of the reflux drum to the flare at the start of the shift. I guess that's what's in the flare. Just a little non-condensible propane vapor," he offered.

"Did anyone check the liquid level in the reflux drum?"

"Yes sir," Bobby responded, finally realizing that I would not be in the plant at 2:00 a.m. if something wasn't very wrong. "Both the inside board-mounted level indicator and the outside level gauge glass both showed the same—a low level in the reflux drum. We even had a low-level alarm come on a few minutes back. We're always trying to. . . ."

Bobby's voice trailed off as I walked out into the humid Texas night. I climbed up to depropanizer reflux drum. From a quarter mile away the radiant heat from the burning flare gas warmed my face. The level in the reflux drum level gauge glass showed the vessel to be almost empty. The vapor vent valve at the top of the reflux drum was half open. Downstream of this valve, the line leading to the flare was covered with ice—a sure sign that a large amount of liquid propane was flashing across the valve.

The depropanizer drum was obviously full of liquid propane. It was so completely full that liquid was being forced out of the top of the drum through the partially open vapor vent valve. When the liquid propane depressured from 300 psig in the reflux drum to 5 psig in the flare line, it autorefrigerated the flare line and caused it to ice up.

Why then, did all three liquid level indicators—the local gauge glass attached to the drum, the board-mounted control room level indicator, and the level alarm—all show a low liquid level in the reflux drum? The answer is that all three instruments depended on the same set of level taps (i.e., connections on the wall of the vessel). When the top level tap plugged with scale, as later proved to be the case, the three instruments sensed a low liquid level in the reflux drum even though it was quite full.

I had the operators reduce the level in the reflux drum by manually opening the propane product control valve. In a very few minutes the darkness descended over the refinery as the flare shrank back to its normal size. I called Mr. Overborne, and was back in bed by 4:00 a.m.

Next morning, back in the plant, I was greeted with the news that the depropanizer reflux pump had broken down. The machinists reported to me that the pump had blown its seal due to cavitation. The cavitation was a consequence of running the pump dry, which in turn was caused by too low a liquid level in the depropanizer reflux drum.

I asked Bobby about the pump failure that night. His reply, I felt, was tinged with just a trace of resentment.

"Well, Mr. Lieberman, after you chewed us out for running with a high liquid level and flaring propane all night, we all decided to keep the reflux drum level nice and low. But since we didn't have any liquid level indication to go by that we could trust, we pulled the level down too low and the reflux pump began to cavitate. I guess that's what damaged the seal on the pump," he concluded.

Level Indication

The key to successful level control is level indication. A simple float-type level sensing installation is shown in Figure 17-1. The liquid level pushes up

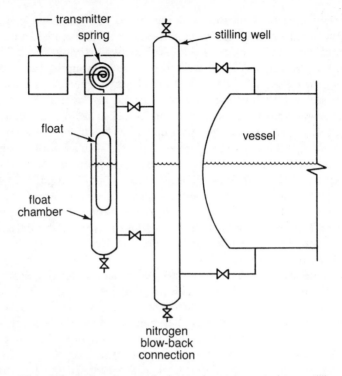

Figure 17-1. A float chamber works best when connected to a stilling well.

the float, which increases the tension of the spring. The spring then alters a pneumatic or electronic signal from the transmitter, which sends the signal to a control valve, or to the instrument panel. Note that the float chamber is indirectly connected to the vessel through an intervening "stilling well." The stilling well is little more than a 4-inch section of pipe. It serves several functions:

▶ Prevents liquid waves in the vessel from bouncing the float and causing an erratic level signal.
▶ Helps keep the float chamber free from scale and dirt that is present in the vessel.
▶ The large-diameter connections between the stilling well and float chamber are less likely to plug than smaller connections that would be made if the float chamber were attached directly to the vessel. The nitrogen connection shown on the bottom of the stilling well is used to blow accumulated debris back into the vessel.

A gauge glass assembly is illustrated in Figure 17-2. Gauge glasses are typically 18 inches high. As in the case of the float chamber, the gauge glasses are connected to a stilling well, rather than directly to the vessel. The important feature of this figure is that the gauge glasses overlap. If the transparent sections of the gauges are not designed to overlap, the liquid level will perversely and invariably hide between adjacent gauge glasses. The designer should provide the valves shown around each glass so that the operators can drain the glass down and watch it refill. Observing if the gauge glass will refill is the proper method to determine if a connection between the stilling well and the glass is plugged.

Figure 17-3 summarizes instrumentation level symbols commonly used by process engineers.

Redundancy in Liquid Level Indication

The problem with the depropanizer reflux drum—remember the liquid level Bobby had so much trouble with—is that both the float chamber and the gauge glasses, as well as the high and low liquid level alarms, were all attached to the same stilling well. When the top tap connecting the vessel to the stilling well plugged, the stilling well showed a low liquid level, although the vessel itself was overflowing with propane.

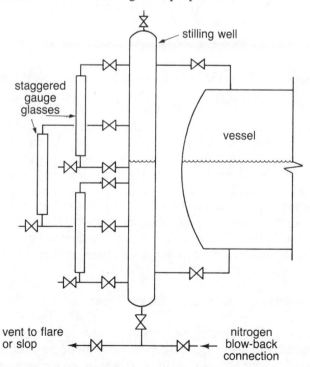

Figure 17-2. Overlapping gauge glasses simplify liquid level observation.

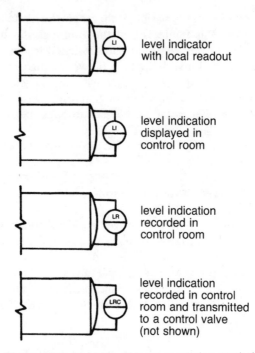

level indicator
with local readout

level indication
displayed in
control room

level indication
recorded in
control room

level indication
recorded in control
room and transmitted
to a control valve
(not shown)

Figure 17-3. Liquid level instrumentation symbols.

A very simple and cost-effective design technique to avoid this difficulty is summarized in Figure 17-4. Two stilling wells are required for a vessel. One senses the liquid level for transmission of a signal to a control valve and the level recorder. The readout from the float chamber on this stilling well should also be displayed on a dial located at the vessel. A second well has staggered gauge glasses connected to it. Also connected to this stilling well are two small float chambers for the high- and low-level alarms.

These facilities enable the outside operator to crosscheck the visible vessel level (which may not be correct) with the level controlling the process (and indicated in the control room) without contacting the control room operator. The latter will have two completely independent checks of the vessel level: the level recorded from the first stilling well, and from the level alarms connected to the second stilling well.

Other Methods of Liquid Level Measurement

The float chamber, although it is widely used in process plants, will not function reliably in many applications. It is up to the process engineer to specify the particular type of level indication required for each service. For example, the float in the float chamber is situated in the liquid and thus may be prone to seizing in a corrosive or fouling environment. Only the process designer can best know the nature of the environment in which the liquid level-sensing device must function. Other methods of liquid level measurement are given here.

Differential Pressure. The pressure at the bottom of a vessel is directly proportional to the liquid height. A pressure-sensing instrument called a "delta-P cell" is connected to the vessel at the lowest level at which a measurement is required. One side of the delta-P cell is connected directly to the vessel at its low point, while the other side is tapped into the vessel at a higher elevation where there is sure to be a vapor space. If the delta-P cell is used in a service that can plug the level taps (such as tar), a purge oil is bled continuously into the low- or high-pressure side of the delta-P cell, while inert gas is used to keep the high- or low-pressure side of the delta-P cell clear of condensing liquid. The main disadvantage of this device becomes apparent when the liquid level in the vessel actually rises above the top tap. The liquid flows into the low-pressure side of the delta-P cell. The pressure difference across the cell is now equalized, and hence the indicated liquid level instantaneously drops from a high level to a very low level.

When using a delta-P cell indicator, never locate its taps across a restriction in the vapor space of a vessel. If this is done, the delta-P cell will measure the pressure drop of the flowing vapors, and add this measurement to the actual liquid level. The result will be an indicated liquid level higher than the actual liquid level.

Conductivity Probes.   Aqueous solutions which are highly corrosive are a good service for conductivity probes. I have used these devices in sulfuric acid alkylation settlers and in rich amine hydrogen sulfide flash drums with excellent results. The conductivity probe only indicates discrete

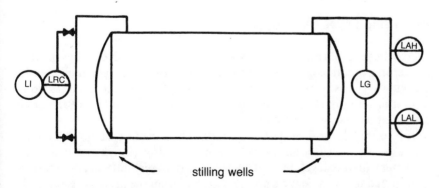

stilling wells

Figure 17-4. Redundancy is the key to reliable liquid level indication.

levels by means of vertically placed electrodes. However, these electrodes may be spaced at one-foot intervals on a single assembly. A well-tuned conductivity probe can differentiate between foam, emulsions, and a settled aqueous phase.

Bubbler. Nitrogen passes through a restriction orifice into a tube that leads into the bottom of a vessel. The nitrogen forces the liquid out of the tube until bubbles escape. The nitrogen pressure downstream of the restriction orifice is equal to the pressure at the bottom of the vessel. Thus, measurement of this pressure with a gauge calibrated in terms of level indicates the height of the liquid level in the vessel. This simple device may only be used when the vessel is held at a constant pressure. A tank open to the atmosphere is a good application for a bubbler level indicator.

Radiation Detectors. A single radiation source is mounted on one side of a vessel, while a number of Geiger-Müller tubes are installed on the opposite side. As the gamma radiation passes thru the liquid in the vessel, they are attenuated. This reduces the pulse rate output of the Geiger-Müller tubes and thus indicates that the liquid level has reached the level of a certain tube.

One company markets a more accurate and potentially less hazardous radiation level detector.[3] It relies on the principle that hydrogen atoms are uniquely able to absorb energy from high-speed neutrons. When hydrocarbons are subjected to fast neutron radiation, the hydrogen absorbs some of the energy. The slow neutrons thus formed are a measure of the density of a fluid in a vessel. The slow neutrons backscatter and hence can be used to detect a liquid level without the necessity of employing a source of radiation powerful enough to pass through the contents of a vessel.

Regardless of the type of radiation level indicator employed, the objective is to determine liquid and/or foam levels without allowing physical contact between the process fluid and instrument components.

Minimizing Level Tap Plugging

For those applications which cannot justify expensive radiation level indicators, the arrangement depicted in Figure 17-5 is recommended for plugging services. I have seen this design successfully employed for liquid level indication in slurry oil service where the solids content of the liquid exceeded two weight percent.

The restriction orifices should be sized so that the flow of purge fluid into the vessel will not cause an appreciable pressure drop (i.e., less than one inch of water) in the level taps. The source of purge oil and gas must be guaranteed to always have a pressure greater than the process vessel. If the purge fluid pressure is momentarily reduced, then the process liquid will

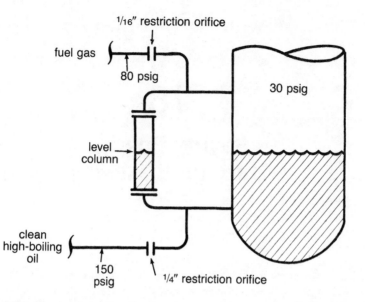

Figure 17-5. Purging level taps in plugging service is required for reliable level indication.

back into the purge fluid piping and plug up the level column, taps, and purge piping.

The process engineer who takes the pains to specify such details will have as his reward the knowledge that he has designed a safe and operable plant.

References

1. Lazenby, B., "Level Monitoring & Control," *Chemical Engineering,* January 14, 1980.

2. Lieberman, N. P., "Instrumenting a Plant to Run Smoothly," *Chemical Engineering,* September 12 1977.

3. "New Detector Spots Foam Levels," *The Oil & Gas Journal,* July 19, 1982, pp. 183-185.

18

Saving Energy
Through Flexibility

When I went to work for Amoco Oil in 1965, natural gas was selling on the Gulf Coast for 22¢ per million Btus. Just 17 years later, the same gas costs $6. Of course, this huge runup in prices is mainly a consequence of politics rather than supply and demand. Although the problem was created by our political leaders, it is the nation's technical leaders who have responded to the challenge. For example, a barrel of crude oil can be refined into finished products using only 80% as much energy as was required a decade ago. This improvement is due to a combination of capital investment and better operating techniques. It is no exaggeration to state that the process design engineer was, and is, a prime mover in energy reduction resulting from both improved operations and design.

One of the underlying principles of energy conservation is to provide plant personnel with the flexibility to achieve energy-efficient operations. By designing plants to function efficiently over a wide range of conditions, the designer gives the operator the opportunity to save energy even at low charge rates.

Turndown in Distillation

A tremendous amount of energy is wasted in process operations because many types of equipment do not function efficiently below a certain rate. A distillation tower is a prime example of this type of problem.

Figure 18-1 shows a typical relationship between tower throughput and tray fractionation efficiency. Note how the efficiency is highest at 80% of flood, (i.e., the usual design rate). This illustrates a general principle applicable to most process equipment: the best energy efficiency is obtained when the rate of operation is closest to the design point.

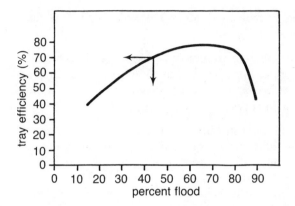

Figure 18-1. Energy is wasted by reduced tray efficiency due to low vapor and liquid rates in a distillation column.

In terms of actual plant operations Figure 18-1 means that a distillation tower must be run at an increased reflux ratio at reduced feed rates. Operating personnel respond to this characteristic of distillation towers by running at fixed reflux rates over a wide range of feed rates. This feature of distillation towers largely accounts for the often-noted problem that energy costs per unit of production increase rapidly at reduced production schedules.

There are a number of tower internal features which the process designer can utilize to increase operating flexibility. For example, in a packed column the turndown ratio (a term used to indicate how far below design throughput equipment can be efficiently operated) of the packing itself may be quite adequate. However, it may be impossible to design a reflux distributor to operate properly at only 20% of the design reflux rate.

A lateral-arm, spray nozzle-type reflux distributor cannot be designed for a 5:1 turndown ratio. At the low end of the operating range, liquid will unevenly trickle out of the nozzles. At maximum flow rates, there will be excessive pressure drop through the nozzles. Even if adequate pressure is available from the reflux pump, the very high pressure drop (in excess of 20-30 psi) will cause the nozzle spray to form a fine mist which will be entrained by the upflowing vapors.

Dual Reflux Distributors

Figure 18-2 shows a field-tested method to deal with the problem of variable reflux rates for a packed column with a spray reflux distributor. Two lateral-arm distributors are used. The nozzles in one of the distributors are designed to pass half the liquid rate with the same pressure drop as the nozzles in the second distributor. The reflux system is then operated as follows:

▶ *Low reflux rates*—minimum flow distributor in service.
▶ *Moderate reflux rates*—maximum flow distributor in service.
▶ *Maximum reflux rates*—both the maximum and minimum flow distributors are put in service.

If the initial liquid distribution is adequate in a packed tower, the packing will fractionate efficiently over a wide range of operating rates. Achieving good initial liquid distribution with dual-spray distributors may add $10,000-30,000 onto the installed cost of a tower. However, if the tower is to operate at reduced throughputs, the energy saved in reboiler heat will quickly payoff this investment.

Turndown in Trayed Columns

Of the most widely used types of trays, bubble caps have the best fractionation efficiency at reduced vapor-liquid rates. Valve-type trays—which have at least 10% greater capacity than bubble-cap trays—have quite a bit less flexibility. Sieve trays characteristically have the poorest turndown ratio.

Although bubble-cap trays are expensive relative to valve trays, they can be made leak proof. It is partially liquid leaking through a tray deck, rather

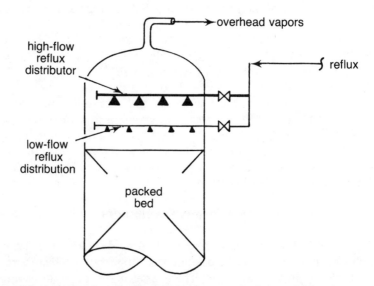

Figure 18-2. A dual-reflux distributor permits a packed tower to fractionate efficiently over a wide range of distillation rates.

than overflowing the tray weir, that accounts for reduced tray efficiency at low vapor rates. The leak-proof nature of bubble-cap trays can thus be used to advantage in certain sections of a trayed column that are subject to low rates. Unfortunately, it is not cost effective, due to the lower capacity and high installment cost of bubble-cap trays, to equip an entire fractionator with bubble-cap decks.

Dual-Cap Valve Trays

One major tray vendor[1] markets a valve tray with an enhanced turndown feature. Each hole in the tray deck is covered by a light and heavy cap, as illustrated in Figure 18-3. At low vapor rates, this light cap is lifted approximately one-quarter inch off the tray deck. Then, as the vapor velocity increases, the light cap is pushed upward against a heavier cap. Finally, at the design vapor velocity, both the light and heavy caps are lifted to their maximum height above the tray deck (about one-half inch). This somewhat complex valve tray is intended to combat unequal vapor distribution at low vapor rates. Motion pictures of operating valve trays (filmed through a glass port) show that the valves on one side of a tray can all be open, while those on the opposite side will be closed. This phenomenon is caused by low pressure drop through the tray combined with a slightly unequal liquid level on the tray deck. The vapor will follow the path of least resistance and open the caps on the tray in the area of lower liquid level, while the other valve caps stay shut.

The unequal vapor distribution causes part of the liquid running across the tray to bypass the upflowing vapors and reduce tray efficiency. Using these caps improves the chances that all the caps on a tray will be at least partially open. Naturally, this type of valve tray is substantially more expensive than the conventional single cap. However, I have seen a large deethanizer retrayed with a double-cap tray with a resulting dramatic increase in fractionation efficiency.

Adjustable Weirs

Assuming that a tray deck is reasonably tight, raising the weir height will increase the tray's efficiency. This is because the greater the depth of liquid on a tray, the more perfect is the degree of mixing between vapor and liquid. Raising the weir height will, however, significantly reduce tower capacity and can lead to premature flooding. For instance, a 2-inch increase in weir height for trays with 24-inch spacing will reduce tower capacity by at least 5%.

Most trays have adjustable weirs. Once access has been gained to a tower, it only takes a few hours to readjust all the weirs. If the tray has been

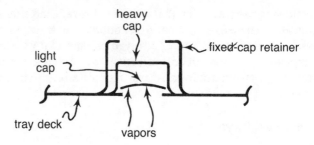

Figure 18-3. The efficiency of a valve tray is enhanced at low rates by using a dual-valve cap assembly.

properly designed, a noticeable improvement in tray efficiency can be expected by raising the weir height when operating at less than 30% of design capacity.

Avoid Leaking Trays

Common valve trays are assembled from sections bolted together inside a tower. The seal between the tray sections is often not very tight. At low vapor rates, tray pressure drop decreases. This increases the rate of liquid leakage through spaces between the tray sections and reduces tray efficiency. Then, to achieve the desired product split, a higher reflux ratio is needed.

To avoid this problem, valve tray sections should be gasketed. I spent five years designing distillation towers before I discovered that this simple, commonsense procedure was not part of a standard tray installation. Tray sections can also be seal-welded in place. This is very time consuming and creates an awkward problem if the trays are ever to be removed. However, contrary to some claims, welded tray sections do not buckle from thermal expansion.

Fired Heaters

Depending on the furnace skin integrity, a great deal of cold air can be drawn into a fired heater through holes in the metal sides or leaks in the roof tiles. This in-leakage of air cools the hot flue gas and hence degrades furnace fuel efficiency. The rate of in-leakage is proportional to the draft (i.e., vacuum) inside the convective section of the heater. At reduced firing rates, and assuming operations personnel remember to pinch off the secondary air registers (see Figure 18-4), the draft in the convective section will increase.

This phenomenon is a principal reason for reduced heater thermal efficiency at low firing rates. To permit operations personnel to adjust the draft in a heater, a stack damper is required. Anyone who owns a fireplace may well wonder why such an obvious and ancient device as a stack damper would ever be omitted from a process heater. The answer is that careless operators have sometimes pinched stack dampers too far closed. The resulting positive pressure below the convective tubes can force hot flue gas to leak outward. This will overheat the steel structure, brickwork, and arch supports of the heater. To avoid this possibility, mechanical designers occasionally delete the stack dampers from new units.

Air Preheaters

A well-designed air preheater will reduce furnace fuel costs by more than 10%. And, as flue gas and air flows drop at reduced firing rates, the temperature of the flue-gas effluent from the preheater will fall, thus indicating an even greater efficiency. Unfortunately, at a temperature of between 300°F and 400°F, the SO_3 dew point of the flue gas is reached. Unless the designer has specified a glass-tube exchange-type air preheater, it is not practical to operate below the SO_3 dew point. Most air preheaters will be subject to severe corrosion by condensing SO_3. To avoid this problem, operators will by-pass cold air around the air preheater. In this way the flue-gas effluent temperature is raised above the SO_3 dew point, although the thermal efficiency of the air preheater is also diminished.

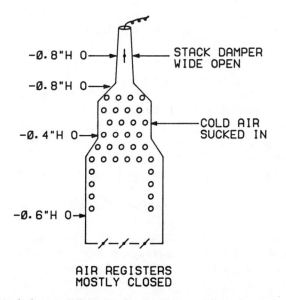

Figure 18-4. A stack damper will increase convective-section efficiency at low firing rates.

A glass-tube air preheater will provide operators the flexibility to run below the flue gas SO_3 dew point. Such a preheater should be specified when two out of three of the following conditions are anticipated:

► Routine operations far below design firing rates.
► Extreme winter temperatures.
► Combustion of high-sulfur liquid fuels.

Heat Exchangers

In theory, heat-transfer coefficients vary to the 0.6 power with mass velocity. In practice, especially in viscous, fouling services, the relationship between overall heat-transfer coefficient and mass velocity is almost linear. In a process plant this means that the thermal efficiency of many heat exchangers does not particularly improve as unit feed rates are cut.

If a heat exchanger consists of two shells operating in parallel, this problem can be effectively overcome by the piping configuration illustrated in Figure 18-5. The valves and lines shown will permit the two parallel shells to be switched to series flow. At flows of 50% of design, this feature will permit design velocities to be achieved through both the shell and tube side of the exchangers. Of course, the pressure drop will be twice design. But, as the series operation will only be employed at reduced flow rates, spare hydraulic capacity will be available.

Laminar Flow

It is good design practice to keep fluid velocities in heat exchangers in the turbulent flow regime. At Reynolds numbers of less than 2100, fluid flow, especially on the tube side of heat exchangers, becomes laminar. Both fouling deposits and heat transfer are adversely affected by laminar flow. Hence, if a heat-exchanger train is to operate properly at reduced flows (in particular, in fouling or plugging services) the velocities at the design rates may have to be quite high. This will waste hydraulic capacity at design flows, but it is the price to be paid for energy-efficient operations at reduced rates.

Centrifugal Pumps

A tremendous amount of electric power is dissipated by throttling on the discharge of motor-driven centrifugal pumps. To overcome this wastage, process designers employ:

► *Turbine-driven spare pumps.* A steam-driven pump can be adjusted to operate at any speed and therefore can eliminate excess pump discharge

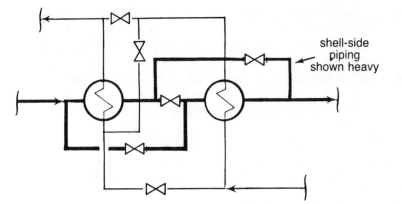

Figure 18-5. Valving parallel exchangers for series operation at reduced rates will improve heat transfer.

pressure. In practice, operators will normally run a motor-driven pump in preference to a steam-turbine drive. The motor-driven pump is just so much simpler to operate.

▶ *Variable-speed motors.* Too expensive.

▶ *Fluid drive coupling.* This device works on the principle of a car's automatic transmission. The fluid drive coupling itself is an inefficient way to transfer torque. Also, it is both expensive and exotic.

One rather prosaic way to reduce electric power consumption by centrifugal pumps is to use a smaller impeller. At reduced throughputs, the lower pump discharge head and flow rate resulting from the smaller impeller will not pose a problem.

If the designer is anticipating frequent low flow rates, he should specify that both a small and large impeller be purchased for each major centrifugal pump. It only takes a shift for a pair of millrights to switch impellers. If the operations supervisor has a smaller impeller stored in the warehouse, he will likely take the initiative to save electricity by switching impellers.

Compressors

To operate efficiently at lower-than-design gas rates, motor-driven (i.e., constant speed) reciprocating compressors should be equipped with adjustable unloading pockets. The required compressor turndown ratio should be specified to the vendor at the time the reciprocating compressor is purchased.

Constant-speed centrifugal compressors are turned down most efficiently by throttling gas flow on the suction, rather than the discharge side of the compressor. Typically, only about half as much compressor energy is wasted by suction throttling as opposed to discharge throttling.

Small (500 hp or less) steam-turbine drivers are best slowed by jet valves. Also called "hand" or "speed" valves, when closed, these valves reduce the nozzle block cross-sectional area inside the turbine's steam chest.

Flexibility Items Which Waste Energy

There are a number of common process design features whose main attraction is to make life simpler for operating personnel. These items, while certainly enhancing unit flexibility, are quite wasteful of energy. A few of these are:

▶ *Pumparound trim water or air coolers.* They permit great flexibility in heat balancing a complex fractionation column. The heat duty of the pumparound trim cooler is, of course, lost to the process.

▶ *Hot-oil circuits.* A source of clean, constant temperature, hot oil supplied from a heater is preferred by operating personnel to using less dependable waste process heat. However, the process heat is free, while the hot oil must be reheated with expensive fuel gas.

▶ *Steam-turbine atmospheric exhausts.* Usually installed for emergency use only, a steam turbine venting to the atmosphere can cost five times as much to operate as a turbine exhausting to a surface condenser.

Omitting these types of equipment from the process design is the only positive method to prevent their use in the field.

Reference

1. F. W. Glitsch & Sons, Inc., *Ballast Tray Design Manual,* Bulletin No. 4900 (Revised), Dallas, Texas.

19

Cost Estimation—
How to Allow
for Installation Factors

The process engineer will, during the course of his design, have to make many decisions on alternative processing routes. The key element in his decision must be cost effectiveness.

The technical literature is replete with detailed methods of cost estimating process equipment. For the purposes of this chapter, the costs assembled in Table 19-1 will orient the novice designer to the approximate price of common types and sizes of plant equipment. The stated values are the purchased, as opposed to the installed, cost of equipment.

A few items worthy of note from Table 19-1 are:

▶ Carbon steel costs are typically half those of stainless steel construction.
▶ Centrifugal, motor-driven pumps are the only type of process equipment which is relatively cheap.
▶ The prices shown for distillation columns are misleadingly low. Most of the cost of a conventional distillation column is associated with the reboiler, condenser, pumps, reflux drum, and internal trays or packing. Equipment costs can be ratioed by the 0.6 power with size to obtain rough prices for larger or smaller sizes.

Installation Costs

The total cost of building a process plant comes as quite a shock to the entry-level process engineer. Most surprising are the tremendous costs associated with erecting, instrumentating, and piping up a relatively inexpensive pump or drum.

Installation factors for several major classes of process equipment are summarized in Table 19-2. The factors are typical but not necessarily

Table 19-1
A Sample of Equipment Costs for Common Process Applications
(1982 Costs)

	Costs ($)
1. Shell and tube heat exchanger, all carbon steel, 16-foot tubes, low-pressure service, 1500 ft² heat exchanger surface..	12,000
2. Same as #1, except all 304 stainless steel construction, 1500-ft² exchanger surface..	22,000
3. A centrifugal pump putting up 100-psi differential head and pumping 200 gpm..	2,500
4. A centrifugal, motor-driver compressor rated for 2000 brake horse-power...	550,000
5. A reciprocating motor-driven compressor rated for 2000 brake horse-power...	700,000
6. A 25-tray distillation column, carbon steel, rated for 300 psig and 8-foot diameter. Does not include reboiler, condensers, trays, pumps, etc.....	130,000
7. Same tower as in #6, 50 trays...	190,000
8. Twenty-five 316 S.S. valve trays for an 8-foot diameter tower............	40,000
9. Twenty-five carbon steel valve trays for an 8-foot diameter tower.......	20,000
10. Two thousand cubic feet of stainless steel, perforated-ring tower packing..	50,000
11. Air-cooled exchanger, carbon steel, 100,000 ft² extended surface, including fan and motor...	140,000
12. A water cooling tower, 20,000 gpm..	400,000
13. A box or cylindrical fired heater, 500-psig tube pressure rating, carbon steel tubes, 100 MM btu hr heat duty absorbed, no air preheater.......	1,200,000
14. Vertical drum, 10,000-gallon capacity, low-pressure service, 304 S.S....	45,000

accurate for a specific case. They will vary with the total cost of each equipment category, that is, the cost for installing 10 identical heat exchangers is less per exchanger than the cost of installing a single exchanger. Also, plant location, labor efficiency, and general economic conditions can markedly affect installation costs. However, the factors shown should be sufficiently accurate to permit selecting between alternatives.

The installation costs are based on the individual pieces of equipment forming part of a major process unit. As such, the cost of the entire process unit is defrayed among the individual drums, compressors, pumps, towers, etc. Hence, the installation costs cover such items as:

▶ Foundations
▶ Process piping and insulation

► Instrument loops
► Control valves
► Utility systems inside the unit
► Control room
► Engineering
► Fire fighting equipment
► Start-up manuals
► Sewers

The installation factors do not cover costs such as steam and power-generation facilities needed to support the process unit's operation or feed and product tankage.

Installation Cost for Individual Process Items

If a $100,000 heat exchanger is to be added to an existing crude unit, the cost of installing it will normally be far less than the $230,000 calculated from Table 19-2. This is because the sewers, control room, and instrument loops are already in place. The foundation, piping, and insulation of the exchanger might cost $50,000-$100,000. It is simply not possible to estimate an installed cost for one or two items of process equipment without considering each case on an individual basis.

Table 19-2
Installation Factors*

Equipment Category	Factor
Fired heaters	3.0
Fin fan air coolers	2.8
Shell and tube heat exchangers	3.3
Shop-fabricated drums	6.6
Shop-fabricated reactors	5.3
Shop-fabricated distillation towers	5.9
Field-fabricated vessels	7.0
Pumps and drivers	4.3
Compressors	2.8
Skid-mounted, preassembled units such as packaged dryers or desalters	3.0
Alloy fractionation trays	2.4

*Note: Multiply equipment quotes received from suppliers by these factors to obtain approximate installation costs. Based on lump sum contract labor and materials.

Utilizing Used Equipment

Almost any category of process equipment may be purchased on the used-equipment market. Some plants have been almost entirely constructed from such equipment. The following recommendations will help avoid trouble:

▶ Purchase of an entire plant, intact, from the original owner is usually o.k.
▶ Purchasing individual pieces of equipment is fraught with hazard.
▶ Used shell-and-tube heat exchangers should be disassembled for inspection prior to purchase. Check that the tube- and shell-side baffles coincide with the as-built drawing.
▶ Plan to retray used distillation towers.
▶ The installation costs for used equipment are frequently higher than for custom-built equipment.

Table 19-3
Typical Costs of Some Common Chemical and Refinery Process Units
(Based on 1982 Costs)

	Cost ($MM)
1. Sour water stripper, 500 gpm	2
2. Aromatics extraction & fractionation, 20,000 BSD	18
3. Depentanizer, 50,000 BSD	3
4. Hydrogen plant based on natural gas feed, 40 MM scf/d	30
5. Propylene concentration unit, 5000 BSD	12
6. Coal gasification, 50,000 MM Btu/d	140
7. Stack gas scrubber, 100,000 lbs/hr of fuel burned	15
8. Gas oil hydrocracker, 30,000 BSD	95
9. Three-way gasoline fractionator, 16,000 BSD total feed	6
10. Delayed coker, 600 T/D	40
11. Light resid desulfurizer, 50,000 BSD	70
12. Claus sulfur recovery unit, 200 LT/D	7
13. Amine stripper, 200 LT/D	6
14. Sulfur plant tail-gas unit, 200 LT/D	4
15. Naphtha reformer, 40,000 BSD	55
16. Crude unit with both atmospheric and vacuum distillation, 200,000 BSD	60
17. Fluid catalytic cracking unit for gas oil, 25,000 BSD	48
18. Butane splitter (ISO & normal) 10,000 BSD	5
19. Sulfuric acid alkylation unit, 15,000 BSD	31
20. Diesel oil or #2 oil hydrosulfurizer, 40,000 BSD	28
21. Caustic regenerator for dissolved mercaptains, 2000 BSD	4
22. Gasoline sweetening, 30,000 BSD	2
23. LPG treater for HD-5, 10,000 BSD	3
24. Mercaptain extraction for alkylation unit feed stock, 18,000 BSD	2

Other than saving procurement time for long lead-time items, it is not often cost effective to purchase used equipment. The fundamental reason is that the major part of the cost of a project is the installation cost. Also, one is never sure as to the actual condition of used process equipment.

Major Plant Costs

Table 19-3 summarizes the actual or estimated prices to build a variety of chemical and refinery process plants. The stated costs do not include associated tankage, utilities, effluent treatment, service roads, general-purpose buildings, spare parts, or all the other components required to complete a major project. These additional offsite facilities are typically considered to add 50% onto the cost of a project.

References

1. Hall, S. R., et al, "Process Equipment Costs," *Chemical Engineering,* April 5, 1982.
2. Guthrix, K. M., "Capital Cost Estimating," *Chemical Engineering,* March 24, 1969.

Glossary

This glossary defines terms used in this book that have developed a meaning peculiar to the process industry. Unlike many other types of technical jargon, process terms are based on rather simple words whose usual meaning has been perverted. For example, a "trip" is an automatic shutdown on a control valve. A "jet" is a device for evacuating a vessel.

AIR FAILURE CLOSE OR OPEN. Refers to the action of a control valve on instrument air failure.

ALARM. A light or siren used to alert operators that an operating parameter is outside its normal operating range.

AMINE. A common solvent used to absorb H_2S and CO_2.

AMPERAGE. The rate at which electrical power is consumed by a motor.

ANNULAR FLOW. Liquid creeps along the walls of a pipe while vapor rushes through the middle of the pipe.

ASPHALTIC. A crude oil containing a large concentration of condensed aromatic rings. The residual portion produces excellent road asphalt.

ASTM DISTILLATION. A standard lab procedure for measuring the boiling range of petroleum distillates.

AUTO IGNITION TEMPERATURE. The temperature at which liquid hydrocarbon will ignite when exposed to air.

BAROMETRIC CONDENSER. A chamber used to condense exhaust steam from a turbine with direct contact with cold water.

BAROMETRIC LEG. The drain line from a condenser under vacuum.

BELL HEAD. The back end of a heat exchanger.

BLIND. A blank metal plate used to positively shut a process line.

BLOCK VALVE. Any valve which is intended to be completely shut or wide open. Not intended to control flows.

BOILER. Fired steam generator.

CAVITATION. The sound that a centrifugal pump makes when vaporization is occurring at its suction.

CHANNEL HEAD. The front end of a heat exchanger.

CHIMNEY TRAY. Collects all liquid inside a column and allows vapor to pass upward without contacting the liquid. Does not fractionate.

CHROME STEEL. Stainless steel, as the term is used in refineries, refers to steel alloyed with nickel and chromium. Chrome steels do not contain nickel.

CLOSED-LOOP CONTROL. A measurement directly changes the position of a control valve without manual intervention.

COLD-OIL VELOCITY. Mass velocity.

COLUMN. Used interchangeably with terms such as tower, fractionator, and splitter.

CONDUCTIVITY CELL. Used to sense the presence of free water or acid in hydrocarbon stream.

CONE-ROOFED TANK. A storage tank with a fixed roof, as opposed to a floating-roof tank.

CONRADSON CARBON. A measurement of the amount of resid in gas oil. A "con" carbon of ½% is usually o.k. for catalytic cracker feed.

CONSERVATIVE DESIGN. Oversizing process equipment to allow for uncertainties.

CONTROL SCHEME. The arrangement of measuring devices and control valves designed to produce the desired heat and material balance through the control of fluid flows.

CONVECTIVE SECTION. That portion of a fired heater where the process fluid recovers heat from flue gas.

CRACKING. Thermal or catalytic conversion of hydrocarbons to coke and lighter products.

CRITICAL SPEED. The rpm at which a piece of rotating equipment will self-destruct.

DELTA P (ΔP). Pressure drop between two points.

DELTA-P CELL. A standard device for measuring a small pressure difference.

DEMISTER. A mesh pad used to promote de-entrainment of liquid droplets from a vapor stream.

DESALTER. Used on crude units to remove salt from crude as a corrosion-control measure.

DIFFUSER. The principal component of a steam ejector or jet.

DOWNCOMER. That portion of a tray that conducts liquid between trays.

DRAW-OFF BOOT. A small drum located below a reflux drum used to accumulate small amounts of water.

DRAW-OFF SUMP. A low point on a tray to which the liquid draw-off nozzle is connected.

DRIVERS. The motor or turbine which provides the torque used to spin pumps and trubines.

EJECTOR. A steam jet used to pull noncondensible gas from a vacuum tower.

ENTRANCE OR EXIT LOSSES. Pressure drops caused by the sudden change of velocity.

EXCELSIOR PACKING. Mats of thin, corrugated, perforated metal sheets used in fractionation.

FIN TUBES. Increases the external surface area of a heat-transfer tube.

FLARE. A high stack used to burn off nonrecoverable gas.

FLASH DRUM. A vessel used to separate vapors and liquids.

FLASH POINT. The temperature at which liquid hydrocarbon will ignite when exposed to a spark.

FLASH ZONE. The open area in a column to which the partially vaporized feed flows.

FLOAT CHAMBER. Common device used to measure liquid levels.

FLOATING HEAD. The internal tube-side head inside a shell-and-tube heat exchanger.

FLOODING. A general term used to describe that condition in a column when it can no longer fractionate due to excessively high vapor and liquid rates.

FLOW-PATH LENGTH. The horizontal distance between the inlet and outlet downcomer across a tray deck.

FLUX. A measurement of the flow of heat between two process stream per unit area of surface.

FOULING. A layer of dirt which restricts heat transfer.

FRACTIONATION STAGE. An equilibrium vapor-liquid flash separation.

GATE VALVE. The most common type of valve used on process units. Usually called a block valve.

GOVERNOR. The device that controls the speed of a turbine.

HEAD. Pressure, as measured in the height of a liquid of a certain specific gravity.

HEAVY OIL. Used as feedstock for the manufacture of lubricating oils and waxes.

HETP. Height equivalent to a theoretical plate. In practice, this is the same a a fractionation stage.

HOLD-DOWN GRID. A screen set on top of a packed bed to surpress upward movement of ring-type packing.

HYDRAULICS. Matters pertaining to the pressure drop of flowing fluids.

IMPELLER. The portion of a pump that develops the liquid head.

IMPINGEMENT. A high-velocity fluid flows against a metal surface.

JET FLOOD. Excessive entrainment of liquid inside a column due to excessive vapor velocity.

JETS. A steam-activated device used to pull a vacuum. Also called an ejector.

KETTLE REBOILER. Characterized by a lack of liquid in the vapor stream flowing back to the column.

LEVEL GAUGE. A device used to measure a liquid level inside a vessel.

LINE LIST. A summary created by the process designer from which process piping and control valves are sized.

LOOP SEAL. Used in a run of piping to prevent vapor from flowing backward in the line.

MASS VELOCITY. Fluid flow as measured in pounds per square foot per second.

MIXED PHASE. Vapor-liquid mixture.

NAPHTHENIC. A hydrocarbon with a saturated ring structure.

NICKEL CONTENT. The most important measurement used to quantify the quality of gas oil for catalytic cracker feed. One ppm or less is a normal target.

NPSH. Net positive suction head. The minimum pressure required at the inlet to a centrifugal pump required for proper operation.

OPEN AREA. The percent of a towers' cross-sectional area available for vapor flow at zero liquid flow.

OPERATIONS. Used interchangeably with the term "process" in most plants.

OPERATORS. The hourly shift workers who man process plants.

ORIFICE DISTRIBUTOR. A static device used to distribute a fluid by means of a pressure drop through openings of a fixed size.

P & IDS. The process and instrumentation drawing. The principal drawing from which the plant is built.

PACKING. The material used in a packed distillation tower. In a trayed tower the liquid phase is continuous; whereas in a packed tower, the vapor phase is continuous.

PARAFFINIC. A straight- or branched-chain hydrocarbon, as opposed to a hydrocarbon containing rings.

PASS PARTITIONS. Baffles in the channel head of a shell-and-tube heat exchanger.

PINCH POINT. That level in a column at which flooding is initiated.

PLOT PLAN. A drawing showing the geographical location of the major items of process equipment.

PNEUMATIC INSTRUMENTATION. Control valves operated and measurements transmitted to instruments by changing air pressure.

PROCESS OPERATIONS. The aspect of a plant referring to its heat and material balance, as opposed to its mechanical intergrity.

PROJECT ENGINEER. The mechanical or civil engineer responsible for implementing the chemical engineer's process design.

PUMPAROUND. Also called intermediate reflux. A circulating stream used to remove heat from a portion of a column.

PURGING. Air-freeing a process vessel with steam or nitrogen.

REBOILER. The heat exchanger which supplies heat to the bottom of a column.

RELIEF VALVE. Also called a "safety," used to protect a vessel from overpressuring.

RESID. Also called black oil or bottoms. The tar remaining behind after the lighter portions of crude are boiled off.

RESTRICTION ORIFICE. A plate with a small hole inserted in a process line to restrict flow.

RINGS. The most common form of packing used in a distillation tower.

RISER. A vertical run of process piping.

ROTOR. The part of a centrifugal compressor that spins.

SACRIFICIAL ANODE. Used to protect heat exchangers from galvanic corrosion.

SEAL DRUM. The vessel used to collect liquid drainage from vacuum surface condensers.

SEAL PAN. A tower internal used to prevent vapor from entering a downcomer.

SEAL (PUMPS). The mechanical device used to prevent fluid leakage along the pump's shaft.

SHUT-IN PRESSURE. A pump's discharge pressure when the outlet block valve is closed.

SIDE-STREAM STRIPPER. A short column attached to a primary fractionator. Used to remove lighter material from products.

SLOW ROLL. The operating practice of allowing a steam turbine to run at a few rpm to keep it warm and ready for service.

SLUG FLOW. A characteristic of mixed-phase flow where the phases separate.

SLURRY OIL. The black, heavy oil produced from the bottom of a fluid catalytic cracking unit.

SOUR WATER. Water drawn off a process unit containing NH_3 and H_2S.

SPARE. A back-up piece of process equipment not normally required.

SPRAY DISTRIBUTOR. Used to distribute liquid laterally by pressure drop through a spray nozzle.

START-UP LINE. A section of pipe used during the commissioning of a plant.

STEAM RACK. A device used on large steam turbines to control the flow of steam by adjusting the nozzle block cross-sectional area.

STRIPPING STEAM. Used in a column to remove lighter boiling material from a product stream.

SUBCOOLING. Lowering the temperature of a liquid stream below its bubble point.

SUCTION STRAINER. A screen used to prevent trash from entering a centrifugal pump.

SUPPORT GRID. Metal bars used to support a bed of packing.

SURFACE CONDENSER. A shell-and-tube heat exchanger used to condense the exhaust steam from a turbine.

SURFACTANTS. A property of liquids which promotes foaming.

SURGE. Unstable operation of a centrifugal compressor.

TAIL GAS. Noncondensible gas to be handled in a vacuum system.

TAPS. Connections in the side of a vessel to which a nozzle is attached.

TEMA (Tubular Exchange Manufacturers Association). An association which publishes the standard manual used in the design of heat exchangers.

THEORETICAL ENGINEER. A derisive term when applied to a process engineer.

THEORETICAL EQUILIBRIUM STAGE. A fractionation stage.

THERMAL CRACKING. The process by which hydrocarbons turn to gas and coke by the action of time and temperature.

THERMOSIPHON. Flow induced by density difference caused by vaporization.

THROTTLING. Controlling the flow of fluid with a valve.

THRUST BEARING. The component of a centrifugal compressor that constrains the axial movement of the rotor.

TOTAL TRAP-OUT. A chimney tray intended to remove liquid totally from a section of a column.

TRAP-OUT TRAY. Collects liquid inside a column so that it can be drawn-off through a nozzle.

TRAY CLIPS. The little clamps which hold a tower internal section together.

TRAY RING. A circumferential strip inside a column used to support trays or a packing grid support. Typically 1-2 inches.

TRAY SPACING. The vertical distance between two trays. Usually 18-30 inches.

TRIP. An automatic device used to shutdown a piece of process equipment to prevent damage to the plant.

TROUGH DISTRIBUTOR. Used to distribute liquid laterally by gravity inside a column.

TUBE SUPPORT BAFFLES. Used in a heat exchanger to improve shell-side heat transfer by increasing fluid velocity.

TURBULENT FLOW. A characteristic of mixed-phase flow where the phases are finely intermingled.

TURNDOWN. The ratio of the minimum stable operating rate to the design rate.

VACUUM TOWER. Any column that operates at a subatmospheric pressure.

VALVE TRAY. The most frequently used distillation device—a tray with a large number of flappers.

VELOCITY STEAM. Steam injected to increase the residence time of oil in a fired heater tube.

VENTURI HOLE. An orifice with a rounded edge used to reduce pressure drop.

VISBREAKER. A process where resid is heated to a temperature at which it thermally cracks with a consequent reduction in viscosity.

VORTEX BREAKER. A small metal cross set over a nozzle inside a vessel used to prevent vortexing of the liquid inside the vessel.

WASH OIL. The vital section of a column above the feed nozzle used to knock back entrained liquid.

WATER TRAP-OUT TRAY. A tower internal used to remove water from inside a tower during normal operation.

WEIRS. That portion of a distillation tray that maintains the liquid level on the tray deck.

WIPER RING. A tower internal device used to prevent liquid from running down the side of a column.

Index